REVISE EDEXCEL GCSE (9–1)
History

MODEL ANSWER WORKBOOK

Series Consultant: Harry Smith

Author: Rob Bircher

Also available to support your revision:

Revise GCSE Study Skills Guide   9781447967071

The **Revise GCSE Study Skills Guide** is full of tried-and-trusted hints and tips for how to learn more effectively. It gives you techniques to help you achieve your best – throughout your GCSE studies and beyond!

REVISE GCSE
Study Skills
GUIDE

Revise GCSE Revision Planner   9781447967828

The **Revise GCSE Revision Planner** helps you to plan and organise your time, step-by-step, throughout your GCSE revision. Use this book and wall chart to mastermind your revision.

REVISE GCSE
REVISION
PLANNER

For the full range of Pearson revision titles across KS2, KS3, GCSE, Functional Skills, AS/A Level and BTEC visit:
www.pearsonschools.co.uk/revise

Contents

A small bit of small print:
Edexcel publishes Sample Assessment Material and the Specification on its website. This is the official content and this book should be used in conjunction with it. The questions have been written to help you practise every topic in the book. Remember: the real exam questions may not look like this.

About your exam

Your Edexcel (9–1) History GCSE comprises **three exam papers**.

Paper 1 ①

Thematic study and historic environment

One option from this list:

- Crime and punishment in Britain, c1000–present *and* Whitechapel, c1870–c1900: crime policing and the inner city
- *Medicine in Britain, c1250–present *and* The British sector of the Western Front, 1914–18: injuries, treatment and the trenches
- Warfare and British society, c1250–present *and* London and the Second World War, 1939–45

This paper is...

 written 1 hour 15 minutes worth 52 marks 30% of the total

Paper 2 ②

Period study and British depth study

One British depth study:

- Anglo-Saxon and Norman England, c1060–88
- The reigns of King Richard I and King John, 1189–1216
- Henry VIII and his minsters, 1509–40
- *Early Elizabethan England, 1558–88

And one period study:

- Spain and the 'New World', c1490–c1555
- British America, 1713–83: empire and revolution
- *The American West, c1835–c1895
- *Superpower relations and the Cold War, 1941–91
- Conflict in the Middle East, 1945–95

This paper is...

 written 1 hour 45 minutes worth 64 marks 40% of the total

Paper 3 ③

Modern depth study

One of:

- Russia and the Soviet Union, 1917–41
- *Weimar and Nazi Germany, 1918–39
- Mao's China, 1945–76
- The USA, 1954–75: conflict and home and abroad

This paper is...

 written 1 hour 20 minutes worth 52 marks 30% of the total

*options covered in this book

Edexcel GCSE (9–1) History is not tiered. This means that all students will sit the same exam papers and will have access to the full range of grades.

9   8   7   6   5   4   3   2   1   U

Command words and mark schemes

Understanding command words

A command word tells you how you should answer a question. Here is an introduction to the most common command words in Edexcel (9–1) GCSE History and some tips on how to answer questions that use them.

Describe

Give the characteristics of something. If you are asked, as in Paper 1, Question 1, to describe two key features, don't waste time explaining your answer in unnecessary detail.

Suggest

Give a possible reason for, or opinion of, something. In Paper 3, Question 3(c), you will need to offer a reason why interpretations may differ and then explain how you've arrived at that reason.

Analyse

Break down the elements of a piece of information and explore their significance in detail. In Paper 2, Question 2, this command word is part of the question stem 'Write a narrative account analysing…'. You should aim to make connections between your points and organise your answer into a logical structure.

Explain

Give reasons why or how. Sometimes, you need to arrive at a judgement, such as in Paper 1, Questions 5 and 6, where you need to explain to what extent you agree with the statement given.

Give

State something. Paper 3, Question 1 asks you to give two things you can infer from a source. You don't have to explain your inference, but you will get a mark for identifying the information in the source that supports your inference.

Understanding mark schemes

Mark schemes tell you what the marker is looking for in your answer. Throughout this book, you will be introduced to using mark schemes alongside exam-style answers. Here are some of the things to look out for.

Mark schemes for short answers

Your answer doesn't need to match these points word-for-word, but it needs to have the same message and use the correct vocabulary. Depending on the question, there may be other possible answers too.

The number in brackets tells you how each mark is awarded.

Question	
1	Describe **two** features of casualty clearing stations on the Western Front. **Target:** knowledge of key features and characteristics of the period. **AO1:** 4 marks.
Marking instructions	

Award 1 mark for identifying a valid feature up to a maximum of two marks. Award 1 mark for supporting information for each feature.
e.g.
- Casualty clearing stations were part of the casualty evacuation chain **(1)**. They were further back from the front line than aid posts and field ambulances **(1)**.
- Injured men did not stay at casualty clearing stations for very long **(1)**. The aim was usually to get them to the point where they could be evacuated to a base hospital **(1)**.

Mark schemes for extended answers

Extended answers are given a level first. Then to award a mark, you need to decide whether the answer is at the top or bottom end of that level.

Level	Mark	Descriptor
2	3–4	• The student explains a similarity by analysing features of the period. [AO2] • Good knowledge and understanding of the period is shown, and the comparison is supported with specific information about the topic. [AO1]
1	1–2	• The student offers a simple or generalised comment about a similarity. [AO2] • Limited knowledge and understanding of the period is shown through generalised information about the topic. [AO1]
	0	No rewardable content.

When you are confident using the extended answer mark schemes in this book, have a look at those on the exam board's website. They contain lots of extra marking information to help you work out what a good answer looks like.

How to use this book

In this book, you will familiarise yourself with the Edexcel (9–1) History GCSE by engaging with exam-style questions, answers and mark schemes. Doing so means you will know exactly what to expect in the exam and, just as importantly, what will be expected of you.

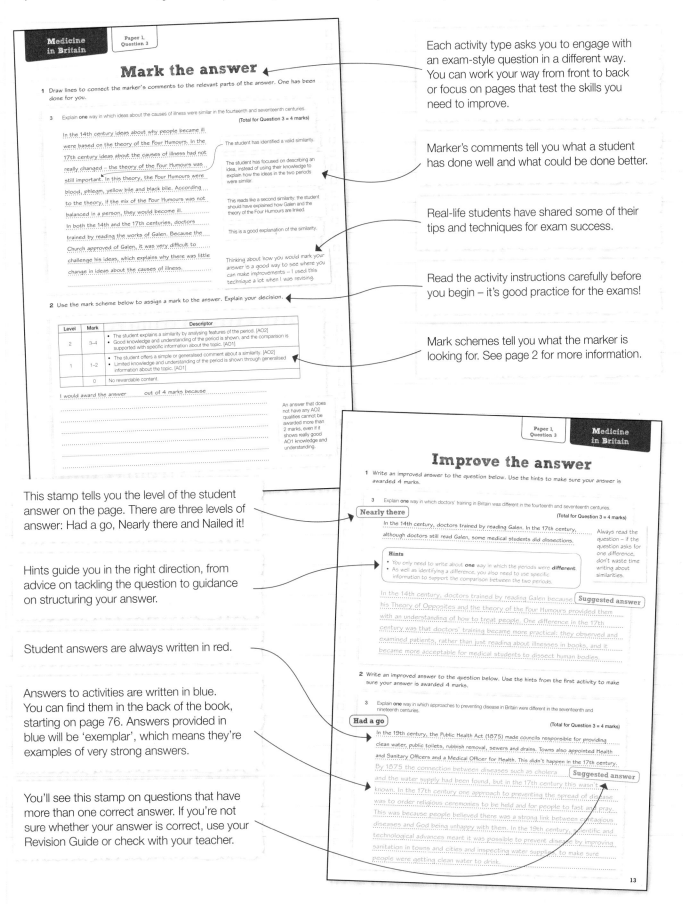

Each activity type asks you to engage with an exam-style question in a different way. You can work your way from front to back or focus on pages that test the skills you need to improve.

Marker's comments tell you what a student has done well and what could be done better.

Real-life students have shared some of their tips and techniques for exam success.

Read the activity instructions carefully before you begin – it's good practice for the exams!

Mark schemes tell you what the marker is looking for. See page 2 for more information.

This stamp tells you the level of the student answer on the page. There are three levels of answer: Had a go, Nearly there and Nailed it!

Hints guide you in the right direction, from advice on tackling the question to guidance on structuring your answer.

Student answers are always written in red.

Answers to activities are written in blue. You can find them in the back of the book, starting on page 76. Answers provided in blue will be 'exemplar', which means they're examples of very strong answers.

You'll see this stamp on questions that have more than one correct answer. If you're not sure whether your answer is correct, use your Revision Guide or check with your teacher.

Sources A and B

Source A: Adapted from the diary of Dr Harvey Cushing, written on 6 June 1915. He was an operating surgeon who worked with the RAMC on the Western Front during the First World War.

> It was the same in all the C.C.S.s*. There was a great tent for reception, with rapid recording of patients —
> some to go on, some to remain, and of these a large quota [share of the men] to the pre-operation room for
> their turn, and others with chest wounds to their proper ward, or still others in critical shape to another place;
> and meanwhile an equally rapid evacuation takes place and a train is ready for 600 cases, and before they
> are off in come another 150, and why can't No. 11 take these, and No. 2 is overcrowded or another behind
> in its work.

* C.C.S. – casualty clearing station

Source B: From the memoirs of John Hayward, a surgeon at a casualty clearing station on the Western Front during the First World War. John Hayward wrote his memoirs after the war and they were published in 1930.

> "Resuss"* was a dreadful place. Here were sent the shocked and collapsed and dying cases, not able to
> stand as yet an operation, but which might be possible after the warming-up under cradles in heated beds
> or transfusion of blood. The effect of transfusion was in some cases miraculous. I have seen men already
> like corpses, blanched and collapsed, pulseless and with just perceptible breathing, within two hours of
> transfusion sitting up in bed smoking, and exchanging jokes before they went to the operating table.

*Resuss – the resuscitation tent

Remember – you can annotate the Source texts as much as you want.
I found it helpful to underline key words and phrases.

Complete the answer

1 Complete the student's answer so that it would be awarded 4 marks.

1   Describe **two** features of the underground hospital at Arras.

(Total for Question 1 = 4 marks)

> Two features have been identified. The question asks you to 'describe' the features, so now you need to add supporting detail to both to get full marks.

Nearly there

Feature 1: The hospital was located in tunnels underneath the town of Arras.

....

....

....

Feature 2: The underground hospital was large and well supplied.

....

....

....

> I wish I'd known you only have to say what each feature is and then find some supporting detail. I wrote about all the features I found, but that meant less time to answer Questions 2(a) and (b), and no extra marks!

2 Complete the student's answer so that it would be awarded 4 marks.

1   Describe **two** features of medical workers on the Western Front.

(Total for Question 1 = 4 marks)

> **Hint**
> • This time the supporting detail has been provided, so now you need to identify the feature being described.

> When I was revising for this paper, I made lists of features for all the main topics, for example, the trench system, the transport system, the different sorts of medical conditions, the stages of treatment, etc. It really helped to answer Question 1.

Nearly there

Feature 1: ....

....

There were around 3000 army medical workers in 1914, and this figure increased to

around 13 000 by 1918.

Feature 2: ....

....

Volunteers were mostly used to drive ambulances and for cooking and cleaning.

Mark the answer

1 Draw lines to connect the marker's comments to the relevant parts of the answer. One has been done for you.

1   Describe **two** features of casualty clearing stations on the Western Front.

(Total for Question 1 = 4 marks)

Feature 1: They were a long way away from the front line, which was the line where soldiers were closest to the enemy.

> This is a correct feature, although the answer should be more specific, e.g. they were located several miles from the front line.

Feature 2: The priority at a CCS was treating men with life-threatening injuries who still had a chance of survival. This was done through a special system where medical workers identified which men were beyond help and which ones could survive.

> The student uses knowledge to provide good supporting information for this feature.

> A valid feature is identified and the student clearly shows good knowledge of the period.

> This supporting information is not relevant because it is not describing a feature of casualty clearing stations.

2 Use the mark scheme below to assign a mark to the answer. Explain your decision.

Question	
1	Describe **two** features of casualty clearing stations on the Western Front. **Target:** knowledge of key features and characteristics of the period. **AO1:** 4 marks.
Marking instructions	

Award 1 mark for identifying a valid feature up to a maximum of two marks. Award 1 mark for supporting information for each feature.

e.g.

- Casualty clearing stations were part of the casualty evacuation chain **(1)**. They were further back from the front line than aid posts and field ambulances **(1)**.
- Injured men did not stay at casualty clearing stations for very long **(1)**. The aim was usually to get them to the point where they could be evacuated to a base hospital **(1)**.

I would award Feature 1 .... out of 2 marks because ....

....

....

I would award Feature 2 .... out of 2 marks because ....

....

....

Improve the answer

1 Rewrite this part of the student's answer to achieve the highest possible mark. This part of the answer relates to Source A on page 4 only.

2 (a) **Study Sources A and B.**

How useful are Sources A and B for an enquiry into the way casualty clearing stations (CCS) treated injured men on the Western Front?

Explain your answer, using Sources A and B and your knowledge of the historical context. (8)

Had a go

There are some good points in this answer, but there is not enough detail.

Source A is useful because it describes the way that casualty clearing stations were divided up and that they were in tents. It also has information about how patients were evacuated once they had been treated: by train. It is useful because it a diary entry and shows it was stressful to work at a CCS.

....

....

....

....

....

....

....

....

....

....

....

....

....

....

....

....

....

....

Our teacher always told us to think about NOP for usefulness of sources: **N**ature, **O**rigin and **P**urpose.

Mark the answer

1 Draw lines to connect the marker's comments to the relevant parts of the answer. One has been done for you. This part of the answer relates to Source B on page 4 only.

2 (a) **Study Sources A and B.**

How useful are Sources A and B for an enquiry into the way casualty clearing stations (CCS) treated injured men on the Western Front?

Explain your answer, using Sources A and B and your knowledge of the historical context.　　　　　　(8)

Source B is written by someone who was a
surgeon at a casualty clearing station, which
means it is a first-hand account by a medical
expert. This means it is likely that his description
is an accurate record of what he experienced,
although his description is written in an emotional
style rather than as a medical account. His memoir
was published, which means it is likely he was not
just writing down his memories for himself but was
thinking about what other people might think as he
was writing them.
Source B contains useful information about how
this casualty clearing station worked, especially
the information about 'resuss': the resuscitation
tent. It tells us that heated beds were used to
warm patients and about blood transfusions. The
description of the effect of blood transfusion
is very interesting and useful because it shows
just how effective blood transfusion could be:
'the effect of transfusion was in some cases
miraculous'. Many more transfusions were possible
on the Western Front due to the development of
better methods of storing blood.

Although NOP is useful for evaluating sources, I tended to focus on it too much. I wish I'd included more contextual knowledge in my answers – basically, what you already know about the topic.

This point about authorship of Source B is developed to make an inference about usefulness.

The student uses knowledge of historical context to support the point about usefulness.

This point about the nature and purpose of Source B is valid but should be developed more to consider what impact it has on the usefulness of the source.

The student has identified useful information from Source B about how this CCS treated injured men. However, the student should then have used contextual knowledge to say what it is about this information that is useful.

This activity continues on page 9

Mark the answer

2 Use the mark scheme below to decide at which **level** the answer on page 8 is working.

Question	
2 (a)	How useful are Sources A and B for an enquiry into the way casualty clearing stations (CCS) treated injured men on the Western Front? **Target:** Analysis and evaluation of source utility. **AO3:** 8 marks.
Level	**Descriptor**
3	• Judgements about usefulness for the specific enquiry in the question are made, which take account of how provenance* affects the usefulness of the source content. Contextual knowledge is used in interpreting the source and making judgements about usefulness.
2	• Judgements about usefulness for the specific enquiry in the question are made. These judgements are supported by comments that are relevant to the sources. Contextual knowledge is used to support comments on the usefulness of the content of the sources and/or their provenance.
1	• A simple judgement is made about usefulness. Supporting comments about the content of the source or provenance are not really developed. The use of contextual knowledge is only limited.
0	No rewardable content.

*Provenance = nature, origin, purpose.

I would award the answer a level .... because ....
....
....
....
....
....
....
....
....
....
....

Remember that a source doesn't have to be written down. It could be a cartoon, a photograph, a poster, a painting, an advert, or an object such as a coin or a postcard.

Find the answer

1 Use the marking instructions below to find the answer that would **not** be awarded the mark.

---

2 (b) **Study Source B.**

How could you follow up Source B to find out more about the way casualty clearing stations treated injured men on the Western Front?

(4)

Detail in Source B that I would follow up:

A | 'The effect of transfusion was in some cases miraculous.'

B | '"Resuss" was a dreadful place.'

C | 'an equally rapid evacuation takes place'

D | 'the warming-up under cradles in heated beds'

> When you are picking the source detail you are going to use, sense-check that you can use it to answer all four parts of Question 2(b).

Marking instructions
Award 1 mark for choosing a detail in Source B that could be developed into a follow-up enquiry.

Answer .... would not get the mark because ....

....

---

2 Look at this student's answer to the first part of the question.

Detail in Source B that I would follow up: 'The effect of transfusion was in some cases miraculous.'

Use the marking instructions to find the answer that would best link to this detail.

Question I would ask:

A | Why did some soldiers need blood transfusions but not others?

B | Were blood transfusions a new treatment?

C | Did soldiers mind having blood transfusions?

D | How often did casualty clearing stations use blood transfusions?

Marking instructions
Award 1 mark for a question which is linked to the detail in Source B that could form the basis of a follow-up enquiry.

Answer .... would get the mark because ....

....

Find the answer

1 Another student has answered the first two parts of a 2(b) question.

Detail in Source B that I would follow up: 'The effect of transfusion was in some cases miraculous.'

Question I would ask: How much blood did casualty clearing stations have stored for transfusions?

Use the marking instructions to find the best source to use to link to the above answers.

What type of source I could use:

A   Army medical records about the amount of blood available to casualty clearing stations

B   Newspaper reports about men who recovered after having blood transfusions

C   Photographs of casualty clearing stations in action

Marking instructions
Award 1 mark for identifying an appropriate source to help answer the selected question.

Answer .... would get the mark because ....

....

2 Another student has written the following answers to part of a 2(b) question.

Question I would ask: What problems occurred with blood transfusions at casualty clearing stations?

What type of source I could use: Letters home by medical workers

Use the marking instructions to find the answer that would **not** be awarded the mark.

How this might help answer my question:

A   The letters might record experiences of transfusions that went wrong.

B   They might show that medical workers found transfusions difficult.

C   The letters home might include graphs of the numbers of unsuccessful blood transfusion.

Marking instructions
Award 1 mark for a response that shows how the source could help answer the selected question.

Answer .... would not get the mark because ....

....

Mark the answer

1 Draw lines to connect the marker's comments to the relevant parts of the answer. One has been done for you.

---

3 Explain **one** way in which ideas about the causes of illness were similar in the fourteenth and seventeenth centuries.

(Total for Question 3 = 4 marks)

In the 14th century ideas about why people became ill were based on the theory of the Four Humours. In the 17th century ideas about the causes of illness had not really changed – the theory of the Four Humours was still important. In this theory, the Four Humours were blood, phlegm, yellow bile and black bile. According to the theory, if the mix of the Four Humours was not balanced in a person, they would become ill.

In both the 14th and the 17th centuries, doctors trained by reading the works of Galen. Because the Church approved of Galen, it was very difficult to challenge his ideas, which explains why there was little change in ideas about the causes of illness.

The student has identified a valid similarity.

The student has focused on describing an idea, instead of using their knowledge to explain how the ideas in the two periods were similar.

This reads like a second similarity: the student should have explained how Galen and the theory of the Four Humours are linked.

This is a good explanation of the similarity.

Thinking about how you would mark your answer is a good way to see where you can make improvements – I used this technique a lot when I was revising.

---

2 Use the mark scheme below to assign a mark to the answer. Explain your decision.

Level	Mark	Descriptor
2	3–4	• The student explains a similarity by analysing features of the period. [AO2] • Good knowledge and understanding of the period is shown, and the comparison is supported with specific information about the topic. [AO1]
1	1–2	• The student offers a simple or generalised comment about a similarity. [AO2] • Limited knowledge and understanding of the period is shown through generalised information about the topic. [AO1]
	0	No rewardable content.

I would award the answer .... out of 4 marks because ....

....

....

....

....

....

....

An answer that does not have any AO2 qualities cannot be awarded more than 2 marks, even if it shows really good AO1 knowledge and understanding.

Improve the answer

1 Write an improved answer to the question below. Use the hints to make sure your answer is awarded 4 marks.

3 Explain **one** way in which doctors' training in Britain was different in the fourteenth and seventeenth centuries.

(Total for Question 3 = 4 marks)

Nearly there

> In the 14th century, doctors trained by reading Galen. In the 17th century,
>
> although doctors still read Galen, some medical students did dissections.

Always read the question – if the question asks for one difference, don't waste time writing about similarities.

> **Hints**
> - You only need to write about **one** way in which the periods were **different**.
> - As well as identifying a difference, you also need to use specific information to support the comparison between the two periods.

....

....

....

....

....

....

2 Write an improved answer to the question below. Use the hints from the first activity to make sure your answer is awarded 4 marks.

3 Explain **one** way in which approaches to preventing disease in Britain were different in the seventeenth and nineteenth centuries.

(Total for Question 3 = 4 marks)

Had a go

> In the 19th century, the Public Health Act (1875) made councils responsible for providing
>
> clean water, public toilets, rubbish removal, sewers and drains. Towns also appointed Health
>
> and Sanitary Officers and a Medical Officer for Health. This didn't happen in the 17th century.

....

....

....

....

....

....

....

....

Complete the answer

1 Complete the student's answer so that it would be awarded 4 marks.

> **3** Explain **one** way in which hospital care in Britain was different in the fourteenth and nineteenth centuries.
>
> (Total for Question 3 = 4 marks)
>
> Hospital care in the 14th century was very religious
>
> ....
>
> ....
>
> ....
>
> In the 19th century, hospitals were about treating ill people so they could recover
>
> ....
>
> ....
>
> ....

2 Complete the student's answer so that it would be awarded 4 marks.

> **3** Explain **one** way in which people's reactions to the plague in Britain were similar in the fourteenth and seventeenth centuries.
>
> (Total for Question 3 = 4 marks)
>
> People's reactions were based on religion
>
> ....
>
> Another example of this similarity is that people in both centuries begged God for mercy
>
> ....
>
> ....

3 Complete the student's answer so that it would be awarded 4 marks.

> **3** Explain **one** way in which people's understanding of the causes of disease in Britain were different in the nineteenth and twentieth centuries.
>
> (Total for Question 3 = 4 marks)
>
> The discovery of the structure of DNA in 1953
>
> ....
>
> This was different from understanding in the 19th century
>
> ....
>
> ....

Find the answer

1 Find the **one** point of additional information that would help answer the question below. Choose **A**, **B**, **C** or **D**. Explain your choice.

4   Explain why there were changes in the treatment of infectious diseases in Britain in the period c1750–c1900.

> You may use the following in your answer:
> * Louis Pasteur's influence
> * smallpox
>
> You **must** also use information of your own.

> Question 4 gives two stimulus points. In order to get more than 8 marks out of the 12 available, the student must also use information of their own.
>
> (Total for Question 4 = 12 marks)

A   Koch's identification of the microbes causing TB and causing cholera

B   William Harvey and discoveries about the circulation of blood

C   Alexander Fleming and the development of penicillin

D   The work of Thomas Sydenham in improving diagnosis

> You don't have to use both or either of the stimulus points provided on the exam paper. If you don't, you need to come up with something else just as good!

Answer .... would be the correct choice because ....

....

2 Find the **one** point of additional information that would help answer the question below. Choose **A**, **B**, **C** or **D**. Explain your choice.

4   Explain why surgery changed so rapidly in Britain in the nineteenth century.

> You may use the following in your answer:
> * James Simpson
> * hygiene
>
> You **must** also use information of your own.

> (Total for Question 4 = 12 marks)

A   The use of chloroform in operations, e.g. Queen Victoria in 1853

B   John Hunter's detailed dissections, improving knowledge of anatomy

C   Lister's development of carbolic acid as an antiseptic

D   The development of sodium citrate to help store blood for transfusion

Answer .... would be the correct choice because ....

....

....

Improve the answer

1 Write an improved answer to the question below. Use the hints to make sure your answer achieves the highest possible mark.

4   Explain why there were changes in the treatment of infectious diseases in Britain in the period c1800–c1900.

> You may use the following in your answer:
> * Louis Pasteur's influence
> * smallpox
> You **must** also use information of your own.

(Total for Question 4 = 12 marks)

Had a go

Jenner developed vaccination just before the 19th century began. He noticed that people who had had cowpox didn't get smallpox. Jenner's experiments with inoculating people with cowpox and then smallpox showed that this method, known as vaccination, could prevent people from catching a disease. Louis Pasteur identified that decay was caused by microbes in the air.

> **Hints**
> * **Explain** the change, don't just **describe** it. Why did these factors cause change?
> * You need to add information of your own to access the highest marks.
> * Remember to link your points together in longer answers.

Complete the answer

1 Complete the student's answer to achieve the highest possible mark.

4 Explain why surgery changed so rapidly in the nineteenth century.

You may use the following in your answer:
- James Simpson
- hygiene

You **must** also use information of your own.

Make sure that your answers are relevant; only write about the period asked about in the question.

(Total for Question 4 = 12 marks)

Hint
- Focus on **change** – explain **why** the 19th century was different from previous periods.

The discovery of anaesthetics was a major breakthrough in surgery because ....

....

....

....

....

....

....

Infection limited the impact of anaesthetics because ....

....

....

....

....

....

....

....

Although there was opposition to Lister's work at first, his ideas led to major changes in ....

surgery because ....

....

....

These developments contributed to rapid change in surgery in the 19th century because ....

....

....

....

....

....

Re-order the answer

1 A student has written a plan to answer this question. Decide which of their points support the statement below and which counter it. Mark each with an S (support) or a C (counter). One has been done for you.

5 'Religion was the main reason why medical treatment made little progress in Britain during the period c1500–c1800.' How far do you agree? Explain your answer.

You may use the following in your answer:
- the Great Plague
- the influence of Vesalius

You **must** also use information of your own.

Questions 5 and 6 ask 'how far you agree' with a statement. This involves making points that support the statement and points that go against it, and then making a judgement about how far the evidence supports the statement.

(Total for Question 5 = 16 marks + 4 SPaG marks)

| S | In the Great Plague, people turned to prayer and fasting to protect them from infection. |

| ☐ | Vesalius's work showed that Galen had been wrong about some important things. The Church approved of Galen. |

| ☐ | People in the 16th century still believed that the king's touch could cure some diseases because they thought the king was chosen by God. |

| ☐ | The Church continued to discourage dissection in the 16th century, and most doctors did not challenge this. |

| ☐ | People responded to the Great Plague in very similar ways to the Black Death: evidence of continuity. |

| ☐ | Not all responses were religious: William Harvey and scientific approach led to new understanding of how the body worked. However, this took time to influence medical treatment. |

| ☐ | Reformation – more than one Church; Renaissance – people wanting to find things out for themselves through experiment rather than just listening to what the Church said. |

| ☐ | Doctors also held on to mistaken scientific ideas, for example the miasma theory about the causes of illness and disease. |

Question 5 is worth 16 marks, plus another 4 for SPaG, so I tried to leave plenty of time to answer and check it properly.

Mark the answer

1 Draw lines to connect the marker's comments about SPaG to the relevant parts of the answer. One has been done for you.

5 'Religion was the main reason why medical treatment made little progress in Britain during the period c1500–c1800.' How far do you agree? Explain your answer.

You may use the following in your answer:
- the Great Plague
- the influence of Vesalius

You **must** also use information of your own.

Questions 5 and 6 each have 4 marks available for Spelling, Punctuation and Grammar (SPaG) and the use of 'specialist terminology'. This means that you should use proper historical terms.

(Total for Question 5 = 16 marks + 4 SPaG marks)

People in the 15th century and in the 17th century both though that religion was very important. It is true medicine did not make much progress this period. for example, there were epidemics of plagues in both centuries, but peoples understanding of what caused plauge and how they should be treated staid the same or nearly. people believed in God being not pleased with people for a cause and prayer and fasting for a treatment. Another similarity that had religion connetions Galen was important still. Galens theory was supported by the church. the church did not want anyone to challenge. What it said was true about religion and the same for medicine causes and treatments.

There are spelling mistakes but these do not get in the way of understanding what the student means to say.

Punctuation is reasonably accurate in this paragraph but there are errors that do make the student's meaning harder to follow.

Good use of some specialist terms, used appropriately, for example epidemic, plague, fasting, prayer, treatment.

Grammar is not always accurate in this section, although the meaning is generally clear.

2 Use the mark scheme below to assign a mark to the answer. There are 4 marks available for SPaG.

Performance	Mark	Descriptor
High	4	• Spelling and punctuation is used with a consistent level of accuracy. A wide range of specialist terms are also used as appropriate.
Intermediate	2–3	• Spelling and punctuation is used with a considerable level of accuracy. A good range of specialist terms are also used as appropriate.
Threshold	1	• Spelling and punctuation is used with a reasonable level of accuracy. Grammar errors sometimes make it difficult to follow the answer. A limited range of specialist terms are used appropriately.
	0	Errors in spelling, punctuation and grammar make it very difficult to understand the answer.

I would give this answer .... out of 4 marks because ....

....

....

19

Improve the answer

1 Write an improved answer to the question below, combining AO1 information with AO2 analysis.

> Questions 5 and 6 target assessment objectives AO1 and AO2.
> * AO1 is about knowledge and understanding of features and characteristics.
> * AO2 is about analysis and evaluation of change and significance.
> * These questions carry 6 marks for AO1 and 10 marks for AO2.

5 'Religion was the main reason why medical treatment made little progress in Britain during the period c1500–c1800.' How far do you agree? Explain your answer.

> You may use the following in your answer:
> * the Great Plague
> * the influence of Vesalius
> You **must** also use information of your own.

(Total for Question 5 = 16 marks + 4 SPaG marks)

Nearly there

In 1543, Andreas Vesalius, an Italian professor of surgery, published his book 'The Fabric of the Human Body'. This book contained many drawings of human anatomy that were based on dissections of corpses. As a result of his detailed anatomical work, Vesalius discovered that some of Galen's teachings were wrong. For example, Galen said the heart was divided by a septum with holes in it that let blood through, while Vesalius showed that this wasn't true. The Church supported Galen's teachings because, although Galen was born before Christianity, he had said that humans had been created so that all their parts worked together, which was what the Church taught too.

> **Hints**
> * All the information in the answer is accurate, but it lacks the analysis and evaluation needed for AO2.
> * Does the Vesalius example support religion being the main reason or not? If it does, explain why it does. If it doesn't, explain why it doesn't.

....

....

....

....

....

....

....

....

....

....

....

Complete the question

1 Fill in the missing stimulus point to complete the question. Choose from the options provided. One has been done for you.

6 'Snow's work connecting disease to water supply was a turning point in improving public health in Britain in the nineteenth century.'
How far do you agree? Explain your answer.

> You may use the following in your answer:
>
> - <u>cholera</u> ....
>
> - ....
>
> You **must** also use information of your own.

Questions 5 and 6 always include **two** stimulus points that you can use in your answer.

(Total for Question 6 = 16 marks + 4 SPaG marks)

- the Great Plague in London
- reports by Edwin Chadwick
- the work of the Royal Society
- Jenner and the development of vaccination

> It's easy to panic and write down everything you know about the topic, but I try to make sure that every point I make refers back to the exact question I've been asked.

2 Fill in the missing stimulus points to complete the question. Choose from the options provided.

6 'The influence of Florence Nightingale was the main reason for improvements in British hospital care c1800–c1900.'
How far do you agree? Explain your answer.

> You may use the following in your answer:
>
> - ....
>
> - ....
>
> You **must** also use information of your own.

(Total for Question 6 = 16 marks + 4 SPaG marks)

- public health during the Boer War
- death rates at Scutari
- the National Insurance Act
- Pasteur's germ theory
- blood transfusion
- the work of Florey and Chain
- Rose Days

3 Use the stimulus points to complete the statement appropriately.

6 '... was a major breakthrough in the prevention of disease in Britain during the period c1700–c1900.'
How far do you agree? Explain your answer.

> You may use the following in your answer:
> - cowpox
> - cholera
>
> You **must** also use information of your own.

(Total for Question 6 = 16 marks + 4 SPaG marks)

Find the answer

1 Read the first paragraph of a student's answer to the question below. Find the **one** comment that does **not** apply to the answer. Choose **A**, **B**, **C** or **D**. Explain your choice.

6 'The Public Health Act 1875 was the most important factor affecting improvements in the prevention of disease in Britain during the period c1700–c1900.'
How far do you agree? Explain your answer.

> You may use the following in your answer:
> - cholera
> - Jenner's vaccination against smallpox
>
> You **must** also use information of your own.

Have a good look at the mark schemes on the exam board's website – it really helped me work out what I had to do in the exam.

(Total for Question 6 = 16 marks + 4 SPaG marks)

Nailed it!

Previously, governments had a 'laissez-faire' attitude to public health, which meant that governments believed they should not interfere in people's lives. The Public Health Act 1875 changed this completely: city authorities now had to inspect and monitor lots of different aspects of public health, including whether housing was overcrowded and whether unsafe food was being sold. City authorities had to provide clean water, sewers and public toilets. As a result, cities had to ensure clean water supplies, which led to reservoirs being constructed, for example in the Elan Valley in Wales to supply Birmingham with clean water. There had been four major outbreaks of cholera in London in the 19th century, causing tens of thousands of deaths. After 1875, there were no further epidemics – the last was in 1866. This suggests that the Public Health Act 1875 was very important in preventing disease.

A | The student has used accurate, relevant information that shows very good knowledge and understanding of this topic.

B | The student's analysis has gone beyond the two stimulus points provided.

C | The student has begun to assess the importance of the statement, which could lead to a judgement.

D | There is explanation of the importance of the points made.

Comment .... does not apply because ....

....

....

Complete the answer

1 Complete the second and third paragraphs of the student's answer from page 22.
Then complete the student's conclusion.

6 'The Public Health Act 1875 was the most important factor affecting improvements in the prevention of disease in Britain during the period c1700–c1900.'
How far do you agree? Explain your answer.

> You may use the following in your answer:
> * cholera
> * Jenner's vaccination against smallpox
> You **must** also use information of your own.

There is no 'right' answer to these questions. The marks are awarded for developing a clear line of argument and providing evidence to support it.

(Total for Question 6 = 16 marks + 4 SPaG marks)

However, the Public Health Act 1875 was not the only factor helping to prevent diseases such as cholera in this period. Jenner's vaccination against smallpox

....

....

....

....

....

....

Another important factor preventing the spread of disease was the influence of Pasteur's germ theory because

....

....

....

....

....

....

....

....

....

The question asked to what extent I agree that the Public Health Act 1875 was the most important factor in preventing disease in this period. My view is that

....

....

....

....

....

Mark the answer

1 Draw lines to connect the marker's comments to the relevant parts of the answer. One has been done for you.

1 Explain **two** consequences of the Gold Rush of 1849.

(Total for Question 1 = 8 marks)

Consequence 1: In April 1849, 100 000 people left eastern USA to travel to California because gold had been discovered there. Thousands travelled along the Oregon Trail and thousands more came from other countries because they dreamed of becoming rich.

Specific information is provided about the Gold Rush.

Good analysis of features explains the consequence for law and order.

Consequence 2: There were significant consequences for law and order, especially in the mining camps. Often the camps were in isolated locations, far away from any law officers. Claim-jumping and fights over claims were common. Bandits (road agents) robbed prospectors. As a consequence of so much lawlessness, mining camps developed their own laws and punishments.

There is no analysis of these details to explain a consequence – the student could have used these details to talk about consequences for settling the West, for example.

The student has clearly identified the feature of the period they are going to analyse.

2 Use the mark scheme below to assign a mark to the answer. Explain your decision.

Level	Mark	Descriptor
2	3–4	• A consequence is analysed using specific features of the period. [AO2] • Good knowledge and understanding is shown, supported by specific information about the topic. [AO1]
1	1–2	• A consequence is stated with a simplified or generalised comment. [AO2] • Limited knowledge and understanding of the period is shown through generalised information about the topic. [AO1]
	0	No rewardable content

Each of the two consequences should be marked separately: 4 marks maximum for each. An answer without any AO2 (talking about consequences) **cannot** be awarded more than 2 marks, no matter how good it is on AO1 (facts and details).

I would award the first consequence .... out of 4 marks because ....

....

....

I would award the second consequence .... out of 4 marks because ....

....

....

....

Improve the answer

1 Write an improved answer to the question below. Use the hints to make sure your answer achieves the highest possible mark.

1   Explain **two** consequences of the American Civil War (1861–65).

(Total for Question 1 = 8 marks)

Had a go

Consequence 1: <u>The Homestead Act (1862) because of opposition from southern states before</u>
<u>the Civil War not being there.</u>

Consequence 2: <u>The cattle industry because of Texas cattle being really cheap because Texas</u>
<u>lost the war at the same time as demand for beef in northern cities increased.</u>

> **Hints**
> - Identify consequences – something that happened **as a result** of the Civil War.
> - Then **explain why** that consequence happened: 'This happened because the Civil War…'; 'This was a consequence of the Civil War because…'
> - Add relevant details to develop your answer and show your knowledge of the period. These should also help explain why the consequence happened.
> - Don't forget to write **two** consequences! The exam paper prompts you to do this.

Consequence 1: ....

....

....

....

....

....

Consequence 2: ....

....

....

....

....

....

....

....

....

Different exam papers in GCSE (9–1) History test different skills.
Discuss consequences here. Do not describe features.

Complete the answer

1 Complete the student's answer to achieve the highest possible mark.

---

1 Explain **two** consequences of the opening of the Bozeman Trail (1863).

(Total for Question 1 = 8 marks)

> **Hints**
> - Underline the command word in your exam questions. This will help you focus your answer on what the question is asking.
> - This question wants you to **explain**, not describe or analyse or make a judgement, so your answer should say **how** something happened **because** of the Bozeman Trail.

Each of the two consequences is marked separately: 4 marks for each. An answer with no AO2 (talking about consequences) **cannot** be awarded more than 2 marks, no matter how good it is on AO1 (facts and details).

Consequence 1: The Bozeman Trail was used by prospectors to reach Montana, where gold

had been discovered in 1862. It crossed Lakota Sioux hunting grounds, which broke the Fort

Laramie Treaty of 1851. This led to Red Cloud's War (1866–68) because

....

....

....

....

....

....

....

....

....

....

Consequence 2: The second Fort Laramie Treaty (1868) was a consequence of the fight over the

Bozeman Trail because

....

....

....

....

....

....

....

I found it really helpful to look at the mark scheme alongside my answers and decide how many marks I would award myself. (The mark scheme for this question is on page 24.)

Re-order the answer

1 A student has written a plan to answer the question below. Number each part (from 1 to 8) to create the best sequence for a successful answer.

2 Write a narrative account analysing the key stages in the growth of the cattle industry in the years 1861–72.

You may use the following in your answer:
- Joseph McCoy and Abilene
- cattle barons

You **must** also use information of your own.

(Total for Question 2 = 8 marks)

☐ Joseph McCoy: stockyards, railroad depot; $5000 on marketing in Texas

☐ John Iliff: first ranch on open range, by 1870 a cattle baron

☐ 1867: railroad reached Abilene

☐ End of Civil War (1865): huge demand for beef in eastern industrial cities

☐ Rise of cattle barons in 1870s: the 'beef bonanza'. Larger and larger herds on open range

☐ Impact of Texas fever: Texans couldn't drive cattle across farmland to Missouri railheads

☐ Problems of cow towns: law and order, long drives

☐ Free grazing land on open range; boom in demand for beef = major increase in investment into cattle ranching

> Making a quick plan is a really good idea before you start writing your answer to Question 2 on Paper 2.

Students may choose whether or not to use the prompts suggested in the question. However, students will only be able to access the top-level marks if they include some information of their own.

Find the answer

1 Find the **one** statement from the student's notes below that does **not** fit into the sequence of events. Choose **A, B, C, D, E, F** or **G**. Explain your choice.

2 Write a narrative account analysing the ways in which early settlements attempted to tackle lawlessness in the years 1835–62.

> You may use the following in your answer:
> - the California Gold Rush (1849)
> - vigilante groups
>
> You **must** also use information of your own.

(Total for Question 2 = 8 marks)

> **Hint**
> - Question 2 requires you to put key events or features together into a clear sequence and show how one key event or feature links to another.

A   Mining settlements grew up rapidly during the Gold Rush of 1849 as thousands of men set up 'camp cities'. These camps were often a long way from any law enforcement, and violence and crime were common.

B   Arguments over claims were a common reason for lawlessness. These included new crimes such as 'claim jumping' and 'salting a claim'. Mining settlements had to find a way to deal with arguments over claims otherwise all claims would just go to whoever was strongest.

C   Mining settlements tackled this lawlessness by appointing a mining recorder, who recorded all mining claims and who had made them.

D   Miners' courts were another way of tackling lawlessness over claims: the camp would appoint a judge to decide who a claim belonged to when miners argued over who had made the claim first.

E   However, there were other problems of lawlessness in the mining camps that miners and prospectors struggled to deal with, especially gangs of road agents and horse thieves.

F   Racist attacks increased as a result of mass settlement in California following the Gold Rush, especially against Indians and immigrant Chinese.

G   Vigilante groups began as a way to deal with a crime wave in San Francisco in 1851. They quickly spread out to Gold Rush mining camps and other settlements across the West as a way of responding to serious crimes.

Answer .... does not fit into the sequence because ....

....

....

....

Improve the answer

1 Write an improved answer to the question below. Use the hints to make sure your answer achieves the highest possible mark.

2 Write a narrative account analysing attempts to solve the problems of farming the Plains in the period 1862–76.

> You may use the following in your answer:
> * barbed wire
> * the Timber Culture Act (1873)
>
> You **must** also use information of your own.

(Total for Question 2 = 8 marks)

Had a go

There were many problems facing homesteaders on the Plains in the 1860s and 1870s. Lack of water meant if it did not rain farmers could not water their crops and had no water for their animals. The Plains were also very difficult to plough because the grass roots formed a mass of tangles under the ground, which were strong enough to break the farmers' iron ploughs. Because there were few trees, farmers had problems fencing their land to separate livestock such as cows from their crops, and building barns and houses. So there were a lot of problems to solve on the Plains in this period.

> **Hints**
> * A **narrative account** is like a story: it needs a beginning, middle and end.
> * The answer needs analysis of how people tried to solve problems and the effect.
> * Make sure your answer is a sequence of key events: it needs to read as a step-by-step account that leads to an outcome.

....

....

....

....

....

....

....

....

....

....

....

....

....

....

Complete the question

1 Complete each part of the question below with a suitable idea. One has been done for you.

> **3** Explain **two** of the following:
>
> - The importance of .... cattle trails .... for the development of the cattle industry in the 1860s.   (8)
>
> - The importance of ....
>   .... for the early settlement of the West. (8)
>
> - The importance of ....
>   .... for changes in the way of life of the Plains Indians, 1876–95.   (8)
>
>   **(Total for Question 3 = 16 marks)**
>
> > In Question 3, you write **two** answers from a choice of **three** questions. Each question will ask you to explain why one thing (such as 'the Homestead Act of 1862') was important for something else (such as 'the settlement of the West').

2 Complete each part of the question below with a suitable idea.

> **3** Explain **two** of the following:
>
> - The importance of the buffalo for the ....
>   ....   (8)
>
> - The importance of the Mormon migration (1846–47) for ....
>   ....   (8)
>
> - The importance of the winter of 1886–87 for ....
>   ....   (8)
>
>   **(Total for Question 3 = 16 marks)**

3 Complete each part of the question below with a suitable idea.

> **3** Explain **two** of the following:
>
> - The importance of the Fort Laramie Treaty (1851) for ....
>   ....   (8)
>
> - The importance of the Exoduster movement (1879) for ....
>   ....   (8)
>
> - The importance of the Johnson County War (1892) for ....
>   ....   (8)
>
>   **(Total for Question 3 = 16 marks)**

Find the answer

1 A student has planned an answer to the **second bullet point** of the question below. Which point is **not** relevant and should **not** be included in the student's final answer? Tick it.

3   Explain **two** of the following:

- The importance of the development of wind pumps (1854) for changes in farming in the West. (8)
- The importance of the Homestead Act (1862) for the settlement of the West. (8)
- The importance of the Battle of the Little Big Horn (1876) for the way of life of the Plains Indians. (8)

(Total for Question 3 = 16 marks)

☐ The homestead plots were affordable, which was important because now many more people could come to settle the West.

☐ Before the Civil War, settlement of the West had been held up by opposition to small homesteads by the southern states.

☐ The Great Plains had never been farmed before and the land was very difficult to plough because of the thickly tangled grassroots beneath the surface.

☐ Almost anyone could file a claim for a homestead, even people who weren't yet citizens of the US. This was important because it encouraged immigrants to settle in the West.

2 A student has planned an answer to the **third bullet point** of the question above. Which **two** points are **not** relevant and should **not** be included in the student's final answer? Tick them.

☐ Custer was defeated because he was reckless in leading just 200 men against 2000 Sioux warriors.

☐ The defeat of the US Cavalry changed US public opinion in favour of crushing Indian resistance.

☐ The US government sent many more soldiers to make sure Indians stayed on their reservations. This had a major impact on the way of life of Indians because they could not hunt for food.

☐ It was important because it meant the Sioux had their weapons and horses taken away from them, which meant they could no longer follow traditional ways of life.

☐ The reason why whites invaded Sioux lands was because they wanted to prospect for gold in the Black Hills.

Questions about the Plains Indians were always my favourite, so I had to be careful not to get carried away and spend too much time on them!

Complete the answer

1 Complete the opening paragraphs of the student's answer to the **second bullet point** in the question below.

---

3   Explain **two** of the following:

• The importance of the development of wind pumps (1854) for changes in farming in the West.   (8)

• The importance of the Homestead Act (1862) for the settlement of the West.   (8)

• The importance of the Battle of the Little Big Horn (1876) for the way of life of the Plains Indians.   (8)

(Total for Question 3 = 16 marks)

Hints

• Your answer must fulfil AO1 (knowledge and understanding) and AO2 (explanation and analysis of the significance and the consequences) to score highly.

• Your answer must focus on **importance**. Do not get sidetracked into evaluating why it is a good or a bad thing.

• Using essay phrases such as 'this was important because…' will help to keep your answer on track and ensure you attempt to explain your ideas.

Before 1862, the US government had tried to encourage people to settle public land in the West by dividing land into 640-acre sections and selling them at $1 per acre. However, this was too expensive for ordinary people. The Homestead Act encouraged ordinary people to settle in the West because

....

....

....

....

....

Nearly half of all the settled land in Nebraska was homestead land, and nearly half of the homesteaders were immigrants to the US. This shows the importance of the Homestead Act for the settlement of the West because

....

....

....

....

....

....

....

Don't forget that in the exam you will need to answer **two** of these 8-mark questions, from a choice of **three**. Make sure you plan your time!

Improve the answer

1 Write an improved answer to the **first bullet point** in the question below. Use the hints to make sure your answer achieves the highest possible mark.

3   Explain **two** of the following:

- The importance of the development of wind pumps (1854) for changes in farming in the West. (8)
- The importance of the Homestead Act (1862) for the settlement of the West. (8)
- The importance of the Battle of the Little Big Horn (1876) for the way of life of the Plains Indians. (8)

(Total for Question 3 = 16 marks)

Had a go

Wind pumps were important for changes in farming in the West because they helped farmers to get more water for their land. They were attached to windmills and some sort of pump then got the water out. This water helped the farmers to grow crops. Another important development in farming was barbed wire. There wasn't enough timber on the Great Plains for fences or for wood to use as fuel. Cattle ranches used barbed wire, too, and they also used wind pumps for water for the cattle.

> **Hints**
> - The answer needs to focus on the development of wind pumps. Including other topics that link to farming wouldn't score marks here.
> - The answer must focus on importance: 'Wind pumps were important because...'
> - A good approach is to think about what changed as a result of wind pumps.

33

Mark the answer

1 Draw lines to connect the marker's comments to the relevant parts of the answer.
One has been done for you.

---

1   Explain **two** consequences of the Soviet invasion of Hungary (1956).

(Total for Question 1 = 8 marks)

Consequence 1: In November 1956, Soviet troops invaded Hungary
to crush Hungarian opposition to Soviet control, which had followed
from reforms introduced by Imre Nagy. Nagy's reforms included free
elections that would threaten the control of the Communist Party in
Hungary and a plan for Hungary to leave the Warsaw Pact.

> Specific information is provided about the Soviet invasion of Hungary.

> One consequence is clearly identified.

Consequence 2: Over 5000 Hungarians died resisting the Soviet
invasion, which led to the United Nations condemning Soviet
actions. However, the international response was not very
strong. A few countries boycotted the 1956 Olympics because
the USSR was taking part, but although the US accepted
80 000 Hungarian refugees it would not send troops to help
Hungarians resist the invasion because of the risk of this turning
into nuclear war with the USSR.

> The student has given specific information that explains the consequence.

> The student has explained why there was an invasion rather than explaining what happened **as a result** of the invasion.

---

2 Use the mark scheme below to assign a mark to the student's answer. Explain your decision.

Level	Mark	Descriptor
2	3–4	• A consequence is analysed using specific features of the period. [AO2] • Good knowledge and understanding is shown, supported by specific information about the topic. [AO1]
1	1–2	• A consequence is stated with a simplified or generalised comment. [AO2] • Limited knowledge and understanding of the period is shown through generalised information about the topic. [AO1]
	0	No rewardable content

> Each of the two consequences should be marked separately: 4 marks maximum for each. An answer without any AO2 (talking about consequences) **cannot** be awarded more than 2 marks, no matter how good it is on AO1 (facts and details).

I would award the first consequence   out of 4 marks because ....

....

....

I would award the second consequence   out of 4 marks because ....

....

....

....

Improve the answer

1 Write an improved answer to the question below. Use the hints to make sure your answer achieves the highest possible mark.

1   Explain **two** consequences of the fall of the Berlin Wall in November 1989.

(Total for Question 1 = 8 marks)

Had a go

Consequence 1: <u>After the Berlin Wall fell in November 1989 that meant East Germany and West</u>

<u>Germany could become one country again.</u>

Consequence 2: <u>The fall of the Berlin Wall also led to the end of the Warsaw Pact.</u>

> **Hints**
> * Identify consequences – something that happened **as a result** of the fall of the Berlin Wall in November 1989.
> * Then **explain why** this was a consequence: 'This was a consequence of the fall of the Berlin Wall because…'
> * Add relevant details to develop your answer and show your knowledge of the period. These should also help explain why the consequence happened.
> * Don't forget to write **two** consequences! The exam paper prompts you to do this.

Consequence 1: ....

....

....

....

....

....

....

....

....

Consequence 2: ....

....

....

....

....

....

....

Different exam papers in GCSE (9–1) History test different skills. Discuss consequences here. Do not describe features.

Re-order the answer

1 A student has written a plan to answer the question below. Number each part (from 1 to 7) to create the best sequence for a successful answer. Then add in the correct dates in the spaces provided.

2 Write a narrative account analysing the key events of the Cuban Missile Crisis (1962).

You may use the following in your answer:
- Cuban revolution
- DEFCON 3 (22 October 1962)

You **must** also use information of your own.

It's a really good idea to review your plan and order your points before you start writing your answer to Question 2.

(Total for Question 2 = 8 marks)

☐ Khrushchev sent a secret message to Kennedy on .... 1962. Khrushchev said he was willing to end the crisis. The next day, JFK sent a response agreeing that the US would not invade Cuba if the missiles were removed.

☐ The Cuban Missile Crisis began when Soviet nuclear missiles were brought to Cuba in secret. On .... 1962, a US U2 spy plane took photographs of missile sites being constructed in Cuba.

☐ Khrushchev reacted to Kennedy's decision by describing the US 'blockade' as an act of aggression. He said that Soviet ships would continue to come to Cuba. On .... 1962, DEFCON 3 was declared. This meant that the US thought war was about to start.

☐ On .... 1962, Khrushchev announced the removal of missiles from Cuba.

☐ Cuba had been closely linked to the US. However, the socialist revolution in Cuba in 1959 made the US an enemy of Cuba. In 1961, the US government backed a failed attempt to overthrow Cuba's socialist government by force.

☐ To end the crisis, the USSR demanded that the US remove its Jupiter missiles from Turkey. On .... 1962, President Kennedy's brother Robert met the Soviet ambassador to the US to agree that this would happen, but that it would not be made public.

☐ President Kennedy was advised by his military chiefs to order an air strike on the missile sites, to prevent the threat of an attack on the US, followed by an invasion of Cuba. However, on .... , JFK decided on a quarantine to stop any Soviet ships reaching Cuba.

Find the answer

1 Find the **one** statement from the student's notes below that does **not** fit into the sequence of events. Choose **A**, **B**, **C**, **D**, **E**, **F**, **G** or **H**. Explain your choice.

2 Write a narrative account analysing the key events of the Soviet response to the Prague Spring (1968).

> You may use the following in your answer:
> - 'socialism with a human face'
> - the Brezhnev Doctrine
>
> You **must** also use information of your own.

(Total for Question 2 = 8 marks)

A	In January 1968, Alexander Dubcek became leader in Czechoslovakia. He was a friend of Brezhnev and a committed communist.
B	Although Dubcek was a communist, Soviet economic and political methods were very unpopular in Czechoslovakia. Dubcek launched reforms.
C	In the 1980s, Gorbachev's 'new thinking' reforms had similar aims to Dubcek's reforms.
D	Dubcek's reforms aimed for 'socialism with a human face' and relaxed political and economic control. This led to the Prague Spring: more freedom of speech resulted in growing criticism of Soviet control and Soviet communism.
E	Brezhnev was alarmed by the Prague Spring. Other communist leaders in Eastern Europe worried that criticism would spread to their countries and would lead to communist parties losing power there.
F	Brezhnev tried but failed to get Dubcek to bring the reforms under control. In August 1968, the USSR ordered troops into Czechoslovakia. Dubcek was arrested.
G	Czechoslovakia had a new leader: Husak. 'Normalisation' introduced strict Soviet control.
H	The Brezhnev Doctrine: the USSR declared the right to invade any Eastern bloc country that threatened the security of the bloc as a whole.

Answer .... does not fit into the sequence because ....

....

....

....

> Question 2 requires you to put key events or features together into a clear sequence and show how one key event or feature links to another.

Improve the answer

1 Write an improved answer to the question below. Use the hints to make sure your answer achieves the highest possible mark.

2 Write a narrative account analysing key events in the creation of Soviet satellite states in Eastern Europe from 1945 to 1949.

You may use the following in your answer:
- the Yalta Conference (1945)
- 'salami tactics'

You **must** also use information of your own.

A narrative account is like a story: it needs a beginning, a middle and an end.

(Total for Question 2 = 8 marks)

Had a go

The USSR thought that Eastern Europe should be in its sphere of influence so Western powers should not have a say in what happened in countries there. In 1946, Churchill made a speech referring to an 'iron curtain' across Europe and warning that the USSR wanted to expand its 'sphere of influence' across Europe. This was important in the development of the Cold War because it added to the US's determination to stop the USSR from taking control, even though in the Yalta conference (1945) the US had agreed to Germany being divided into zones of occupation.

Hints

- The answer so far is not organised into a sequence. Although key events are referred to, they are not all relevant or accurate, and the student has not made links between them.
- Make sure your answer reads as a step-by-step account that leads to an outcome (a result at the end of the process, for example that by 1950 the USSR controlled a bloc of Eastern European countries).

....

....

....

....

....

....

....

....

....

....

....

....

....

Complete the question

1 Complete each part of the question below with a suitable idea. One has been done for you.

3   Explain **two** of the following:

- The importance of US possession of .... the atom bomb .... for
relations between the US and the USSR.   **(8)**

- The importance of .... in Berlin (1958–61) for
increasing tensions between East and West.   **(8)**

- The importance of .... (1968) for Soviet control of
Eastern Europe.   **(8)**

(Total for Question 3 = 16 marks)

| the Brezhnev Doctrine | ~~the atom bomb~~ | nuclear non-proliferation |
| Tehran Conference | the refugee problem | the formation of NATO |

In Question 3, you write two answers from a choice of three options. The options will each ask you to explain the importance of **an event/person/development** for **a situation** or **an unfolding development**.

2 Fill in the missing situation or unfolding development to complete the question. Choose from the options provided.

3   Explain **two** of the following:

- The importance of Cominform (1947) for ....
.... **(8)**

- The importance of the launch of Sputnik (1957) for ....
.... **(8)**

- The importance of the 'Velvet Revolution' (1989) for ....
.... **(8)**

(Total for Question 3 = 16 marks)

the collapse of Soviet control of Eastern Europe	increasing Soviet influence in Eastern Europe
increasing de-Stalinisation in Eastern Europe	the US policy of brinkmanship
Soviet relations with Cuba	the development of the arms race between the US and the USSR

Our teacher gave us a copy of the specification for GCSE (9–1) History at the start of year 10. It was useful to see what we needed to know about different topics.

Find the answer

1 A student has planned an answer to the **first bullet point** of the question below. Which point is **not** relevant and should **not** be included in the student's final answer? Tick it.

3   Explain **two** of the following:

- The importance of the Marshall Plan (1948) for the development of the Berlin Crisis. **(8)**
- The importance of the Cuban Missile Crisis (1962) for attempts to reduce the threat of nuclear war. **(8)**
- The importance of Soviet economic weakness for the collapse of the Soviet Union. **(8)**

(Total for Question 3 = 16 marks)

☐ The Marshall Plan was $13 billion of economic aid from the US to help rebuild Europe after the Second World War, including rebuilding Germany.

☐ It made sense for the British and US zones in Berlin to be combined: Bizonia. This area was included in the Marshall Plan.

☐ The Soviet Union wanted Germany to be weak and divided so that it would not be able to attack the USSR again; the Marshall Plan threatened the USSR's aims for Germany.

☐ In August 1945, the USSR's Gosplan was instructed to prepare a new Five Year Plan for economic recovery.

☐ The Soviet Union suspected that the US wanted to create a successful and separate West Germany. This was important in its decision to block supply routes to West Berlin.

2 A student has planned an answer to the **third bullet point** of the question above. Which **two** points are **not** relevant and should **not** be included in the student's final answer? Tick them.

☐ Economic weakness meant the USSR could not keep up with the US in military spending, while the US poured money into missile technology.

☐ This was important because public opinion in countries such as the UK and Germany was often against nuclear weapons.

☐ The USSR was bogged down in a war in Afghanistan that was deeply unpopular with many families and young people.

☐ In the Soviet Union and across Eastern Europe, economic problems meant that people did not have a good standard of living. This was important because it made many people unhappy with their lifestyles.

☐ Gorbachev's economic reforms – perestroika – were designed to fix the problems of the Soviet economic model. He felt this could only work if people were free to criticise the older ways of doing things: glasnost. However, criticism increased far beyond Gorbachev's expectations.

Complete the answer

1 Complete the student's answer to the **first bullet point** in the question below.

3 Explain **two** of the following:

- The importance of the Marshall Plan (1948) for the development of the Berlin Crisis. **(8)**
- The importance of the Cuban Missile Crisis (1962) for attempts to reduce the threat of nuclear war. **(8)**
- The importance of Soviet economic weakness for the collapse of the Soviet Union. **(8)**

(Total for Question 3 = 16 marks)

In response to the Marshall Plan being introduced in March 1948, in April 1948 the USSR made it much more difficult for transport to .... enter West Berlin – the start of the Berlin Crisis of 1948. The US's Marshall Plan was $13 billion of economic aid that countries could ... sign up to in order to rebuild after the war. It was important for the development of tensions between the superpowers because ....

....

....

....

....

....

....

....

....

The Comecon countries of Eastern Europe were forbidden by Stalin from signing up to the .....

Marshall Plan. This was because ....

....

....

....

....

....

....

....

....

....

> We're always told to 'remember to PEE' – **P**oint, **E**vidence, **E**xplain – in History exam questions.

> I used a minute per mark as my guide for planning time: so 8 marks meant around 8 minutes' writing time. This means that you don't end up with too little time to answer the 16-mark questions – and it also leaves you time to check your answers at the end.

Improve the answer

1 Write an improved answer to the **second bullet point** in the question below. Use the hints to make sure your answer achieves the highest possible mark.

---

3   Explain **two** of the following:

• The importance of the Marshall Plan (1948) for the development of the Berlin Crisis.   (8)

• The importance of the Cuban Missile Crisis (1962) for attempts to reduce the threat of nuclear war.   (8)

• The importance of Soviet economic weakness for the collapse of the Soviet Union.   (8)

(Total for Question 3 = 16 marks)

Had a go

The Cuban Missile Crisis was about the missiles that the Russians had put on Cuba, very close to the US. When the US found out that the missiles were there, it nearly led to nuclear war. One of the options that President Kennedy had to consider was airstrikes on the missile bases in Cuba. That could have led to a war starting with Russia. So the Cuban Missile Crisis didn't reduce the threat of nuclear war, it increased the threat instead.

> **Hints**
> • Answers to these questions have to focus on **importance**: 'the Cuban Missile Crisis was important for attempts to reduce the threat of nuclear war because...'
> • This response has not answered the question because the student doesn't include enough knowledge about what happened after the Cuban Missile Crisis.
> • Think about what changed as a result of the Cuban Missile Crisis and how this led to the threat of nuclear war being reduced.

....

....

....

....

....

....

....

....

....

....

....

....

....

....

Mark the answer

1 Use the mark scheme below to assign a mark to the answer. Explain your decision.

5   (a)   Describe **two** features of the Babington plot (1586).   (4)

Feature 1: One feature was that Mary, Queen of Scots, was executed after the plot was found out. She was executed by being beheaded.

Feature 2: The plot involved an invasion of England by the Duke of Guise. The plan was for the Duke to kill Elizabeth and put Mary, Queen of Scots, on the throne.

Marking instructions
Each valid feature should be awarded 1 mark, up to a maximum of 2 marks. Each feature should be awarded a second mark for supporting information. E.g.   • Mary, Queen of Scots, was involved in the plot (1 mark), which was shown by Babington's letters to Mary (1 mark).

I would award the first feature   out of 2 marks because

....

I would award the second feature   out of 2 marks because

....

2 Use the mark scheme below to assign a mark to the answer. Explain your decision.

5   (a)   Describe **two** features of Elizabethan society.   (4)

Feature 1: One important feature was the Privy Council. This was made up of members of the nobility who helped to govern the country and took account of what was happening in parliament.

Feature 2: There were tenant farmers and also merchants – they could be very wealthy.

Marking instructions
Each valid feature should be awarded 1 mark, up to a maximum of 2 marks. Each feature should be awarded a second mark for supporting information. E.g.   • People had to show care for those below them (1 mark). Landowners had a duty of care for their tenants if, for example, there was a harvest failure (1 mark).

I would award the first feature   out of 2 marks because

....

....

I would award the second feature   out of 2 marks because

....

Complete the question

1 Use the student's answer to complete the question. Include dates where possible.

5 (a) Describe **two** features of .... (4)

Nailed it!

Feature 1: A new prayer book was introduced in 1559, called the Book of Common Prayer, which had to be followed by all clergy. The wording in the prayer book was made so that Protestants and Catholics could both use it and understand different things.

Feature 2: A second feature was the Act of Supremacy. Elizabeth was named as Governor of the Church of England. Her father, Henry VIII, had named himself Supreme Head of the Church of England. Governor was a title that showed Elizabeth was more tolerant of religious differences in England.

2 Use the student's answer to complete the question. Include dates where possible.

5 (a) Describe **two** features of .... (4)

Nailed it!

Feature 1: Two of the main rebels were Thomas Percy, Earl of Northumberland, and Charles Neville, Earl of Westmorland. Both of them were Catholics who owned huge areas of land in the north, but who had lost a lot of their influence at court.

Feature 2: A second feature was that many northern landowners did not join the revolt, mainly because they had gained a lot of wealth from Henry VIII's dissolution of the monasteries and did not want to have to give it back if England became Catholic again. Examples were landowners in Lancashire and Cheshire.

3 Use the student's answer to complete the question. Include dates where possible.

5 (a) Describe **two** features of .... (4)

Nailed it!

Feature 1: Parliament saw vagrants as a threat to public order and wanted to deter vagrancy. Vagrants were whipped and had a hole put in their ears for a first offence, imprisoned if arrested for vagrancy again and given the death penalty for a third offence.

Feature 2: A second feature was helping the 'impotent poor'. A national poor rate was introduced and local authorities (for example, JPs and parish councils) had to keep a poor register and find work for able-bodied poor people.

Complete the answer

1 Use the marking instructions below to complete the student's answer so that it would be awarded 4 marks.

5 (a) Describe **two** features of the Puritan challenge in the 1560s. (4)

Feature 1: Puritans wanted a simpler style of worship that purified churches of Catholic 'graven images' such as ....

....

Feature 2: Puritans refused to wear the vestments required by the Royal Injunctions because ......

....

....

Marking instructions
Each valid feature should be awarded 1 mark, up to a maximum of 2 marks. Each feature should be awarded a second mark for supporting information. E.g. • Puritans wanted to live in a 'more godly' society (1 mark). An example of what would make society more 'godly' was banning 'sinful' activities such as gambling or cock fighting (1 mark).

2 Use the marking instructions below to complete the student's answer so that it would be awarded 4 marks.

5 (a) Describe **two** features of school education during Elizabeth's reign (1558–1603). (4)

Feature 1: Parish schools were for children up to the age of 10 years. They were owned by ....

....

Feature 2: Grammar schools ....

....

....

Marking instructions
Each valid feature should be awarded 1 mark, up to a maximum of 2 marks. Each feature should be awarded a second mark for supporting information. E.g. • Very few children in Elizabethan England went to school (1 mark). No one believed there was any point educating anyone but the children of rich people, since it was thought no one else would need it (1 mark).

Find the answer

1 A student has planned an answer to the question below. Find the **one** point that is **not** accurate, and the one point that is **not** relevant. Explain your choices.

5 (b) Explain why there was an increase in poverty in Elizabethan England, 1558–88. (12)

You may use the following in your answer:
- rural enclosure
- bad harvests

You **must** also use information of your own.

You should only include information that is **accurate** and **relevant** in your answer.

A | Enclosure meant poor people couldn't use common land any more.

B | Monasteries had helped poor people in the past, but they had been dissolved by Henry VIII in the 1530s.

C | England's population grew from 30 million in 1551 to 42 million in 1601.

D | People who refused to pay the poor rates could be put in prison after the 1576 Poor Relief Act.

E | There were harvest failures in 1562, 1565, 1573 and 1586, which drove up food prices and meant subsistence farmers couldn't grow enough to live on.

The information that I think is not accurate is point .... because ....

....

The information that I think is not relevant is point .... because ....

....

2 Find the **one** point of additional information that would **not** help answer the question above. Tick it.

☐ The growth in the triangular trade, developed by John Hawkins

☐ Increasing demand for land due to population increase

☐ Economic recessions caused by trade embargoes

☐ Sheep farming, because it meant less food was grown

Paper 2, Question 5(b) gives you two stimulus points, but you need to add your own information as well as (or instead of) these two points.

Improve the answer

1 A student has written the first paragraph of an answer to this question. Use the hints below to improve it.

5   (b)   Explain why the Spanish Armada was defeated in 1588.   (12)

> You may use the following in your answer:
> - the Battle of Gravelines (8 August 1588)
> - the weather
>
> You **must** also use information of your own.

> I wish I'd practised writing exam answers in my revision! I learned loads of facts and dates, but sometimes I just wrote down everything I could remember about a topic rather than using what I knew to actually answer the question.

Had a go

The Armada was defeated for many reasons. One was the Battle of Gravelines. Another was that English ships were better armed and equipped. Another was that bad weather hit the Spanish ships when they were trying to retreat. The English had better tactics, too – they could sail close to the Spanish ships and fire on them, but not get so close that the Spanish soldiers on the ships could get across to the English ships. The Battle of Gravelines had fireships. These were important in winning the battle, which the English did, led by Francis Drake.

> **Hints**
> - Focus on **explaining** – the answer so far has too much description.
> - Make a clear argument. The answer above is not very clear. Draw attention to the points you are making by using one paragraph per point and saying things like 'A second reason was that…'
> - For each point you make, say why this point helps to explain the defeat of the Armada.
> - Support your points with detail or examples that show you understand this topic.

....
....
....
....
....
....
....
....
....
....
....
....

Mark the answer

1 Draw lines to connect the marker's comments to the relevant parts of the answer. One has been done for you.

---

5 (b) Explain why Drake circumnavigated the globe (1577–80). (12)

> You may use the following in your answer:
> - the Battle of San Juan de Ulúa (1568)
> - profits
>
> You **must** also use information of your own.

The main reason why Francis Drake sailed round the world was not because he was an explorer but because he planned to steal treasure from the Spanish. The Spanish were mining silver and gold in South America (the Spanish Main) and then shipping it back to Spain. Drake intercepted Spanish treasure ships and stole tons of silver and gold – in fact 26 tons of silver and half a ton of gold, as well as jewels and other treasure. However, Drake could not return to England with his treasure, across the Atlantic, because Spanish ships were waiting for him. He went up the west coast of the Americas, tried to find a way back east through the North-West passage but couldn't find it (it was only a myth then), and so was forced to try to sail back west, through Indonesia and round Africa.

This suggests that the most important reason for Drake's voyage was profit. He had an excellent record as a privateer and that meant many rich people were prepared to invest in his voyage, in return for a share of the profits. When Drake finally got back to England in September 1580, Elizabeth's share of the profits was more than enough to pay off England's national debt at the time. It was this enormous profit that made Drake so famous.

Evidence of analytical explanation, as the student is considering which reasons might be more important than others. Let's see if this gets developed later.

Detailed knowledge shown here; shame the student did not link more closely to the question, e.g. as evidence of profits from the raids for investors.

Clear focus on the question from the start of the answer. Introduces own knowledge and understanding: potential for Level 4.

The student is spending far too much time describing what Drake did here: I can't give this any marks because it isn't explaining anything.

Excellent use of AO1 knowledge to support an AO2 analytical explanation.

Find the answer

1 A student has planned an answer to the question below. Find the **one** point that is **not** accurate, and the **one** point that is **not** relevant. Explain your choices.

5 (c)(i) 'Religious divisions were Elizabeth's main challenge when she became queen in 1558.'
How far do you agree? Explain your answer.   (16)

> You may use the following in your answer:
> • Catholic grievances
> • Philip II
> You **must** also use information of your own.

Paper 2, Question 5(c) gives you two stimulus points, but you must also use your own information as well as (or instead of) these two points.

A	Catholic nobles like the Nevilles and Percys resented their loss of influence under Elizabeth.
B	In 1566 the pope instructed English Catholics not to attend Church of England services.
C	People believed that priests could guide them in life and protect them from bad consequences.
D	Philip II of Spain had been married to Mary, Queen of Scots, which gave him a claim to the English throne.
E	By 1570, England was surrounded by potentially hostile Catholic powers. The Pope also excommunicated Elizabeth in 1570.

The information that I think is not accurate is point .... because ....

....

....

The information that I think is not relevant is point .... because ....

....

2 Find the **one** point of additional information that would **not** help answer the question above. Explain your choice.

A	Legitimacy, as a daughter of Anne Boleyn	D	The Puritan challenge
B	England's financial weakness	E	The Peace of Troyes
C	The Auld Alliance		

Answer .... would not help answer the question because ....

....

....

Re-order the answer

1 A student has written a plan to answer this 5(c)(i) question. Decide which of their points support the statement below and which counter it. Mark each with an S (support) or a C (counter). One has been done for you.

5 (c)(i) 'Religious divisions were Elizabeth's main challenge when she became queen in 1558.'
   How far do you agree? Explain your answer. **(16)**

> You may use the following in your answer:
> * Catholic grievances
> * Philip II
>
> You **must** also use information of your own.

> **Hint**
> * In deciding 'How far do you agree?' for question 5(c)(i) and (ii), you should consider points that support the statement and points that do not support, or counter, the statement. You then use this evidence to reach your overall judgement.

| S | One of Elizabeth's first acts as queen was the religious settlement of 1559, which tried to establish a form of religion that would be acceptable to both Protestants and Catholics. This shows how important it was to her to deal with religious differences. |

| ☐ | There were very significant financial problems in 1558: the Crown was £300,000 in debt and debasing the value of England's coinage had resulted in inflation. |

| ☐ | When Anne Boleyn was executed in 1536, Henry VIII had excluded Elizabeth from the succession. Although he reversed this decision before his death, many people continued to doubt Elizabeth's legitimacy. |

| ☐ | As well as Catholic grievances, Elizabeth also faced a Puritan challenge to her religious settlement. |

| ☐ | In 1566, the Pope instructed English Catholics that they were not to attend Church of England services. |

| ☐ | Mary, Queen of Scots, was a focus for Catholic plots against Elizabeth because she was a Catholic with a legitimate claim to the throne. |

> These questions are worth 16 marks, so I tried to leave plenty of time to tackle them properly.

Complete the answer

1 Use the prompts below to complete the first two paragraphs of the student's answer.

5 (c)(i) 'Religious divisions were Elizabeth's main challenge when she became queen in 1558.'
How far do you agree? Explain your answer. (16)

> You may use the following in your answer:
> * Catholic grievances
> * Philip II
> You **must** also use information of your own.

*For questions like this, you don't just have to write about the issue in the question. It's asking you if religious divisions were **most** important, so you need to discuss the other challenges Elizabeth faced as well and then explain which was most significant.*

Catholic challenges to her rule were major problems for Elizabeth, both from Catholics in England and from European Catholic nations such as France and Spain. Catholics in England refused to acknowledge Elizabeth's right to rule England because

....

....

....

....

....

....

....

....

However, Catholic grievances and Puritan opposition were not the only challenges facing Elizabeth when she became queen. There were very significant financial problems: the Crown was £300 000 in debt and debasing the value of England's coinage had resulted in inflation. The financial position was a challenge for Elizabeth because

....

....

....

....

....

....

....

....

....

....

Find the answer

1 Use the hints below to find the answer that is the focus of the following question.
Choose **A**, **B**, **C** or **D**. Explain your choice.

---

5 (c)(i) 'Religious divisions were Elizabeth's main challenge when she became queen in 1558.'

How far do you agree? Explain your answer. (16)

> **Hints**
>
> Questions for Paper 2 test your knowledge of the period **and** your ability to interpret this information using 'second order concepts', such as:
> - Causation – what were the reasons or causes?
> - Consequence – what happened as a result?
> - Significance – what was most important?
> - Continuity and change – what changed, and what continued as before?
> - Similarity and difference – what was the same, and what was different?

A	Causation	C	Significance
B	Consequence	D	Continuity and change

This question focuses on concept .... because ....

....

....

---

2 Use the hints above to find the answer that is the focus of the following question.
Choose **A**, **B**, **C** or **D**. Explain your choice.

---

5 (c)(i) 'Mary, Queen of Scots' involvement in the Babington plot was the main reason for her execution in 1587.'

How far do you agree? Explain your answer. (16)

A	Causation	C	Significance
B	Consequence	D	Continuity and change

This question focuses on concept .... because ....

....

....

Complete the question

1 Fill in the missing prompts to complete the questions. One has been done for you.

Question 5(c) always has two options to choose from, so you can pick the one you can answer best. Each question has two prompts to help you out, but don't forget to use what you've learned in class as well.

5 (c)(ii) 'Rural enclosure was the main reason for the increase in poverty during 1558–88.'

How far do you agree? Explain your answer. **(16)**

You may use the following in your answer:

- bad harvests ....
- ....

You **must** also use information of your own.

5 (c)(ii) 'Lack of planning was the main reason for the failure of Virginia.'

How far do you agree? Explain your answer. **(16)**

You may use the following in your answer:

- ....
- ....

You **must** also use information of your own.

2 Add appropriate statements to complete the questions. Make sure your statements are relevant to the prompts.

5 (c)(ii) ....

....

How far do you agree? Explain your answer. **(16)**

You may use the following in your answer:
- the raid on Cadiz
- commercial rivalry

You **must** also use information of your own.

5 (c)(ii) ....

....

How far do you agree? Explain your answer. **(16)**

You may use the following in your answer:
- the excommunication of 1570
- recusants

You **must** also use information of your own.

53

Re-order the answer

1 A student has written a plan to answer this 5(c) question. Decide which of their points support the statement below and which counter it. Mark each with an S (support) or a C (counter). One has been done for you.

---

5 (c)(ii) 'Mary, Queen of Scots' involvement in the Babington plot was the main reason for her execution in 1587.'
How far do you agree? Explain your answer.

(16)

> You may use the following in your answer:
> - the threat from Spain
> - Elizabeth's excommunication (1570)
>
> You **must** also use information of your own.

> **Hint**
> - In deciding 'How far do you agree?' for question 5(c)(i) and (ii), you should consider points that support the statement and points that do not support, or counter, the statement. You then use this evidence to reach your overall judgement.

| S | Mary was sentenced to death because Babington's letters, intercepted by Walsingham, gave clear evidence that she was involved in the plot and supported it. |

| ☐ | Previous plots involving Mary had also been uncovered by Walsingham without them leading to Mary's execution, e.g. the Throckmorton plot of 1583. |

| ☐ | There had been strong demands from parliament for Mary to be executed before (e.g. in 1572 after the Ridolfi plot), but Elizabeth had been too worried about Catholic unrest to execute her. The Babington plot forced her to overcome these concerns. |

| ☐ | Previous plots had shown just how major a threat Mary posed to Elizabeth. However, what made the situation so serious in 1587 was that England was virtually at war with Spain (since 1585) and Philip II had supported the plot. |

| ☐ | In 1570 the Pope excommunicated Elizabeth in order to encourage Catholics to oppose her reign. Because of this there were many plots against Elizabeth, including the Babington plot. |

| ☐ | After the Babington plot, persecution of Catholics in England intensified, which showed that Elizabeth's government was no longer worried about upsetting Catholics. This was a factor in executing Mary. However, this persecution had begun after the Ridolfi plot of 1571 and intensified after the Throckmorton plot of 1583. |

Improve the answer

1   Write an improved answer to the question below. Use the hints to make sure your answer achieves the highest possible mark.

5   (c)(ii) 'Mary, Queen of Scots' involvement in the Babington plot was the main reason for her execution in 1587.'
How far do you agree? Explain your answer.   (16)

You may use the following in your answer:
* the threat from Spain
* Elizabeth's excommunication (1570)

You **must** also use information of your own.

I found these question prompts really useful. They helped me frame my response and gave me clues about what needed to be in my answer.

Had a go

The Babington plot was the main reason why Elizabeth decided to have Mary, Queen of Scots, executed, because there was evidence that showed she had encouraged it. The plot was discovered by Sir Francis Walsingham, who found letters from Babington that showed Mary's involvement. The letters also listed other Catholics who wanted Mary to replace Elizabeth, so that England had a Catholic queen and not a Protestant one. Other less important reasons why Mary was executed were the threat from Spain and Elizabeth's excommunication (1570).

Hints
* This answer contains some good knowledge, but it needs to analyse the information to explain its importance.
* The answer mentions other points that could be used as evidence to support the statement or argue against it, but the student needs to develop these points.

....
....
....
....
....
....
....
....
....
....
....
....
....
....

Mark the answer

1 This simplified mark scheme for Question 5(c) has some information missing. Complete it by putting the information below into the correct gaps. One has been done for you.

Accurate and relevant information is included that shows good understanding of the topic.

There is explanation of why reasons were important, very clear to read and linking to the question all the way through.

There is an overall judgement with some justification, but the justifications aren't always very good.

There is an overall judgement that is fully justified in a convincing way.

There is explanation of why reasons were important, but the explanation doesn't really link to the question.

The answer doesn't make any judgement at all.

Some accurate and relevant information is included.

~~The answer is very simple and not at all developed.~~

> The more you get to know what examiners are looking for, the better your answers will become.

Level	Mark	Descriptor
4	13–16	• AO2: .... • AO1: Accurate and relevant information is included that shows a really good understanding of lots of different features of the topic. • AO1: ....
3	9–12	• AO2: There is explanation of why reasons were important, which generally links to the question, but not always very clearly. • AO1: .... • AO1: ....
2	5–8	• AO2: .... • AO1: .... • AO1: There is a judgement about the most important reason for the execution, but the answer just says it without backing it up.
1	1–4	• AO2: The answer is very simple and not at all developed. • AO1: Only very limited information about the topic is included. • AO2: ....

Complete the answer

1 Complete the student's answer so that it would be awarded 4 marks.

Study Source C below and then answer Question 1.

Source C: A picture by Wolfgang Willrich in 1938 showing the ideal Aryan family.

1 Give **two** things you can infer from Source C about the Nazi view on women and the family in the 1930s.

Complete the table below to explain your answer. **(Total for Question 1 = 4 marks)**

(i) What I can infer:

The Nazis believed that women's role was to have children.

Details in the source that tell me this:

A large family is shown

(ii) What I can infer:

The Nazis believed that boys and girls should take part in different activities.

Details in the source that tell me this:

Remember, there's never one single correct answer in History: it's all about being able to **justify** your point with **evidence**.

Mark the answer

1 Draw lines to connect the marker's comments to the relevant parts of the answer.

Study Source D below and then answer Question 1.

Source D: From a Ministry of Propaganda order, March 1934

> Attention! On Wednesday 21st March, the Fuhrer is speaking on all German [radio] stations from 11am to 11:50am ... All factory owners, stores, offices, shops, pubs and flats must put up speakers an hour before, so that the whole workforce can hear.

1 Give **two** things you can infer from Source D about how the Nazis used media to influence people's attitudes.

Complete the table below to explain your answer.

(Total for Question 1 = 4 marks)

(i) What I can infer:

Radio was important for Nazi propaganda.

....

Details in the source that tell me this:

The Nazis used different media for propaganda,

including newspapers, plays, art, books and

films. Yet radio was the most important, perhaps

because lots of people had a radio in their

house (this was before TVs) and on the radio

people could listen to Hitler actually talking,

which was a powerful experience.

(ii) What I can infer:

There was an important speech by Hitler on 21st

March 1934.

Details in the source that tell me this:

It gives the date in the source and also the time

so people knew they had to listen.

Marker's comments:

This is not a valid inference: the student has identified information provided by the source rather than going beyond what the source says.

This is a valid inference to make for 1 mark.

Unfortunately, the student has not backed up the valid inference with supporting detail selected from the source. Instead, they have used their own knowledge to explain why radio was important. No marks can be awarded for this.

This is not a convincing supporting statement to back up a point about importance. Selecting relevant quotes from the source would have been a better approach here.

Hints

Examiners are always looking for ways to give you marks if they possibly can, which is why it is better to write something rather than nothing.
- The 4 marks available for Question 1 are split into 2 marks for each inference.
- The first mark is for identifying a valid inference – something that you can correctly infer from the source. This should not be something that is stated directly.
- The second mark is for supporting detail to back up the inference. That detail needs to come from the source.
- A good way to back up an inference is to use a quote from the source.

Find the answer

1 Find the **one** point of additional information that would help answer the question below. Choose **A**, **B**, **C** or **D**. Explain your choice.

---

2 Explain why there was an economic recovery in the Weimar Republic in the period 1924–29.

> You may use the following in your answer:
> * the introduction of the Rentenmark
> * American loans
> You **must** also use information of your own.

(Total for Question 2 = 12 marks)

A	The Treaty of Versailles
B	Labour service
C	Rearmament
D	The Dawes Plan

> Question 2 asks the student to explain why a change happened. The question provides two stimulus points with suggested topics to write about, but in order to get more than 8 marks out of the 12 available, the student must include information of their own.

> I thought the more I wrote, the more marks I'd get but examiners are looking for really specific things – and waffle isn't one of them!

Answer .... would be the correct choice because ....

....

....

---

2 Find the **one** point of additional information that would **not** help answer the question below. Choose **A**, **B**, **C** or **D**. Explain your choice.

---

2 Explain why there were changes in the lives of women in Nazi Germany 1933–39.

> You may use the following in your answer:
> * Nazi organisations for women and girls
> * the introduction of marriage loans
> You **must** also use information of your own.

(Total for Question 2 = 12 marks)

A	The League of German Maidens	C	Awards for numbers of children
B	Nazi ideals on women's clothing, hair and use of make-up	D	Kinder, Küche, Kirche

Answer .... would not help answer the question because ....

....

....

Improve the answer

1 Write an improved answer to the **first bullet point** in the question below. Use the hints to make sure your answer achieves the highest possible mark.

2 Explain why support for the Nazi Party grew in the period 1929–32.

You may use the following in your answer:
- the Wall Street Crash (1929)
- the influence of the SA

You **must** also use information of your own.

Make sure you **explain** reasons for the change. Don't just describe what happened!

(Total for Question 2 = 12 marks)

Had a go

The Wall Street Crash (1929) was the collapse in the value of US stock exchange shares. The German banks lost so much money that people worried they would lose their savings and rushed to get them out of the banks. To stay in business, banks demanded that businesses pay back loans to them, which meant industries, farms and other businesses ran out of money and went bust or sacked workers. This caused high unemployment, which meant few people had any money to buy products, businesses couldn't make money and went bust, meaning more unemployment. More unhappy poor people supported the Communist Party, worrying the middle class and richer people, who started to support the Nazis. That is one reason why the Nazi Party got more support.

Hint
- Keep referring back to the question: you need to explain why support for the Nazi Party grew, not why unemployment grew, for example.

....

....

....

....

....

....

....

....

....

....

....

....

....

Find the answer

1 Read the first paragraph of a student's answer to the question below. Find the **one** comment
that is **not** relevant to the answer. Choose **A**, **B**, **C** or **D**. Explain your choice.

2 Explain why Hitler came to be appointed Chancellor of the Weimar Republic in January 1933.

> You may use the following in your answer:
> • Hitler's campaigning
> • von Papen
> You **must** also use information of your own.

(Total for Question 2 = 12 marks)

Nailed it!

One of the main reasons for Hitler being made Chancellor in 1933 was that the Nazis were
successful in getting money to fund their election campaigning from big industrial companies
such as Krupp and Bosch. The reason why these industries gave money to the Nazis was
because they were concerned that the communists would get control of Germany and take
over their companies. Without this money, the NSDAP would not have been able to afford
mass rallies, posters and leaflets. For example, for the 1932 Reichstag election, the NSDAP
printed and distributed 600 000 copies of their economic programme, which set out how the
Nazis would deal with Germany's economic crisis.

Marking instructions for Level 4
Level 4 answers (10–12 marks) will: • go beyond the two stimulus points provided, using the student's own information   • not just describe points but use them to 'explain why'   • use precisely selected information that is used to answer the question directly   • make clear arguments that are always closely linked to answering the question.

A   The student has used accurate, relevant information that
     shows very good knowledge and understanding of this topic.

B   The student's analysis has gone beyond the two stimulus points provided.

C   The student has successfully 'explained why' Hitler became Chancellor in 1933.

D   The answer is clearly written so it is easy to follow the argument.

Comment   is not relevant because ....

....

....

....

....

....

Mark the answer

1 Study Source E on page 74. Draw lines to connect the marker's comments to the relevant parts of the answer. One has been done for you.

3 (a) **Study Sources E and F.**

How useful are Sources E and F for an enquiry into the ways that Hitler undermined democracy in Germany in 1933–34?

Explain your answer, using Sources E and F and your knowledge of the historical context.

(8)

> **Hint**
> - The answer extract here only covers Source E. In the exam you need to write about the usefulness of both of the sources you are given.

Source E is useful because it suggests that Hitler wanted to violently destroy both the communist opposition and the Social Democratic opposition to the Nazis rather than rely on democratic elections to remove opposition. This is shown in Source E by Hitler saying 'The German people have been soft too long', meaning that the German people had allowed the communist threat to grow in popularity in elections rather than stamping it out. Source E is also useful because of its origin: a police chief who was directly involved in the investigation of the Reichstag Fire and who was a witness to Hitler's reaction. The use of the word 'screaming' in Source E suggests that Diels was quite critical of Hitler's reaction, because it suggests that Hitler was out of control. However, there are also problems of usefulness to do with Source E's origin and purpose. It is a memoir written after the end of the war, when people in Diels' position needed to show they were not Nazi war criminals.

Starts with a clear focus on utility (usefulness)

Could have developed this point about how memoirs (written long after the event) affect usefulness

Uses NOP (nature, origin, purpose) to judge usefulness

Develops point with a relevant extract from the source

Develops point using own knowledge

Links to usefulness for an enquiry into the ways Hitler undermined democracy

Develops point about origin with a clear reason about how provenance affects usefulness

This activity continues on page 63

Mark the answer

2 Use the mark scheme below to decide at which level the answer on page 62 is working.

Remember, in the exam you should write about both of the sources you are given.

Question	
3(a)	How useful are Sources E and F for an enquiry into the ways that Hitler undermined democracy in Germany in 1933–34? Explain your answer, using Sources E and F and your knowledge of the historical context. **Target:** Analysis and evaluation of source utility. **AO3:** 8 marks.
Level	**Descriptor**
3	• Judgements about usefulness for the specific enquiry in the question are made, which take account of how provenance* affects the usefulness of the source content. Contextual knowledge is used in interpreting the source and making judgements about usefulness.
2	• Judgements about usefulness for the specific enquiry in the question are made. These judgements are supported by comments that are relevant to the sources. Contextual knowledge is used to support comments on the usefulness of the content of the sources and/or their provenance.
1	• A simple judgement is made about usefulness. Supporting comments about the content of the source or provenance (nature/origin/purpose) are not really developed. The use of contextual knowledge is only limited.
	No rewardable content.

*Provenance = nature, origin, purpose.

I would award the answer a level .... because ....

....

....

....

....

....

....

....

....

....

....

....

....

....

....

Complete the answer

1 Study Sources E and F on page 74. Complete the student's answer to achieve the highest possible mark.

3 (a) **Study Sources E and F.**

How useful are Sources E and F for an enquiry into the ways that Hitler undermined democracy in Germany in 1933–34?

Explain your answer, using Sources E and F and your knowledge of the historical context. (8)

Source E is useful because it suggests that Hitler wanted to violently destroy both the communist opposition and the Social Democratic opposition to the Nazis rather than rely on democratic elections to remove opposition. This is shown in Source E by Hitler saying 'The German people have been soft too long', meaning that the German people had allowed the communist threat to grow in popularity in elections rather than stamping it out.

Source E is also useful because of its origin: a police chief who was directly involved in the investigation of the Reichstag Fire and who was a witness to Hitler's reaction. The use of the word 'screaming' in Source E suggests that Diels was quite critical of Hitler's reaction, because it suggests that Hitler was out of control. However, there are also problems of usefulness to do with Source E's origin and purpose. It is a memoir written after the end of the war, when people in Diels' position needed to show they were not Nazi war criminals.

> **Hints**
> • Try this approach for usefulness: write about how the contents of the source make it valuable (what it says) and then add in a second point explaining usefulness in terms of NOP – **N**ature, **O**rigin, **P**urpose.

Source F is useful because it suggests ....

....

....

....

....

....

Another reason that Source F is useful is because ....

....

....

....

....

....

....

....

....

Find the answer

1 Which **two** student answers below are **not** key differences between Interpretations 1 and 2 on page 75? Explain your choices.

3 (b) Study Interpretations 1 and 2. They give different views about the ways that Hitler undermined democracy in Germany in 1933–34.

What is the main difference between the views?

Explain your answer, using details from both interpretations. (4)

A   While Interpretation 2 is quite modern (2004), Interpretation 1 is from a longer time ago.

B   While Interpretation 1 says the Nazis were responsible for the Reichstag Fire, Interpretation 2 suggests that it was the communists who had burned down the Reichstag.

C   Interpretation 2 focuses on the Decree of the Reich President for the Protection of People and State while Interpretation 1 does not.

D   Interpretation 1 suggests that the Nazi response was 'spontaneous and largely irrational' while Interpretation 2 describes an effective propaganda campaign.

E   Interpretation 2 considers the reaction of German people to the Reichstag Fire while Interpretation 1 focuses on the Nazi leadership's reaction to the fire.

Hints

- Remember: a **source** is something written or created at the time. An **interpretation** is something written or created later.
- The two interpretations on your exam paper will be specially selected so that they give two different views on a topic. That doesn't mean that examiners will only be looking for one correct answer about the difference between them, but it does mean that there definitely will be a difference for you to write about.
- You only need to point out the differences between the interpretations, not say which one you think is right.

Answers   and   are not key differences between the two interpretations because ....
....
....
....
....
....
....
....
....
....

Mark the answer

1 Study Interpretations 1 and 2 on page 75. Draw lines to connect the marker's comments to each of the three different answers below.

---

3 (b) Study Interpretations 1 and 2. They give different views about the ways that Hitler undermined democracy in Germany in 1933–34.

What is the main difference between the views?

Explain your answer, using details from both interpretations.

(4)

Answer 1

Interpretation 1 is about who was responsible for the Reichstag Fire because it starts 'whoever was responsible'. Interpretation 2 isn't about who was responsible because it says the 'German Bolsheviks' were to blame.

This answer gives a difference but it is only a superficial one – not really a key difference in views. There is support for this difference: a quote from Interpretation 2.

Answer 2

A key difference is that Interpretation 1 suggests the Nazi response to the Reichstag Fire was unplanned and chaotic while Interpretation 2 focuses on the Nazis' effective propaganda campaign.

This answer has identified a key difference between the interpretations but has not supported this difference.

Answer 3

Both the interpretations say the Nazis were frightened of the communists but Interpretation 1 says the Nazis were frightened of an uprising while Interpretation 2 says the Nazis were frightened 'that public disorder would occur'.

This answer gives support for the difference identified, but the difference identified is not a valid one.

---

2 Use the mark scheme below to assign a mark to each answer. Explain your decisions.

Level	Mark	Descriptor
2	3–4	• The student has analysed the interpretations, identified a key difference and supported it.
1	1–2	• The student has briefly analysed the interpretation, but the identified difference is only about surface details, or not supported.
	0	No rewardable content.

I would award Answer 1 .... out of 4 marks because ....

....

I would award Answer 2 .... out of 4 marks because ....

....

I would award Answer 3 .... out of 4 marks because ....

....

Improve the answer

1 Write an improved answer to the question below. Use the interpretations on page 75 and the hints below to make sure your answer is awarded 4 marks.

3 (b) **Study Interpretations 1 and 2. They give different views about the ways that Hitler undermined democracy in Germany in 1933–34.**

What is the main difference between the views?

Explain your answer, using details from both interpretations. (4)

Nearly there

The main difference is that Interpretation 1 suggests the Nazi response to the Reichstag

Fire was unplanned and chaotic while Interpretation 2 focuses on the Nazis' effective

propaganda campaign.

> **Hints**
> * Has the student identified a valid difference between the two interpretations?
> * Is this a key difference or only a superficial difference?
> * Does the student explain the difference by referring to both interpretations, or just one?
> * Has the student supported the difference by describing or quoting what the interpretations say?

....

....

....

....

....

2 Use the same hints to improve this next answer to the same question so that it would be awarded 4 marks.

Nearly there

The main difference is that Interpretation 2 focuses on how German people supported the

Nazis in using undemocratic methods to prevent a communist uprising. It says that ordinary

Germans 'were impressed by the proofs of the dastardly Communist plot' and thought it

was right that the Nazis should be able to lock up communists without a trial.

....

....

....

....

....

....

Find the answer

1 Which **two** student answers below are **not** valid reasons for differences between Interpretations 1 and 2 on page 75? Studying Sources E and F on page 74 will also help.

3 (c) Suggest **one** reason why Interpretations 1 and 2 give different views about the ways that Hitler undermined democracy in Germany in 1933–34.
You may use Sources E and F to help explain your answer.   (4)

A The interpretations may be different because the authors have a different emphasis. Interpretation 1 is looking at how the Nazis responded to the Reichstag Fire while Interpretation 2 is looking at how German people responded to anti-communist propaganda from the Nazis.

B The interpretations may be different because one author did not understand the sources, for example Interpretation 1 didn't understand that Source F proves the Nazis did plan carefully because they actually started the Reichstag Fire.

C The interpretations may be different because they are extracts from longer pieces of writing: Interpretation 1 is looking at what happened before the Reichstag fire decree, and Interpretation 2 is looking at what happened after the Reichstag fire decree.

D The interpretations may be different because Interpretation 2 is written by one person while Interpretation 1 was written by two people, which might have meant they had to compromise on their interpretation, which would explain why it isn't very interesting.

E The interpretations may be different because they are based on different sources. For example, Interpretation 1 is supported by Source E, which describes an out-of-control Hitler screaming about a communist plot. Source F would not support Interpretation 1, but it could give some support to Interpretation 2, which describes the Nazis' effective, well-planned propaganda campaign.

Answers .... and .... are **not** valid reasons for differences between Interpretations 1 and
....
2 because
....
....
....
....
....
....
....
....
....
....
....

Mark the answer

1 Study Sources E and F and Interpretations 1 and 2 on pages 74–75. Draw lines to connect the marker's comments to each of the three different answers below.

3 (c) Suggest **one** reason why Interpretations 1 and 2 on give different views about the ways that Hitler undermined democracy in Germany in 1933–34.
You may use Sources E and F to help explain your answer. (4)

Answer 1 | They are looking at two different aspects of this topic: one is about the way the Nazis responded and the other is about how German people responded.

This answer has identified a valid reason for a difference but has not analysed the interpretations to explain the reason.

Answer 2 | Interpretation 1 could be based on Source E because that source shows that Hitler's response to the Reichstag Fire was 'drastic' and 'irrational', as Source E describes Hitler as 'screaming' that all communists should be shot or hanged.

This answer has identified a valid reason for a difference between the interpretations but has not explained how the reason links to the interpretations or supported this explanation.

Answer 3 | Interpretation 1 and Interpretation 2 might be different because they are based on different sources.

This answer has explained a connection between a source and an interpretation but has not used analysis to give a reason for a difference between the two interpretations.

Level	Mark	Descriptor
2	3–4	• The student gives a reason for the difference that is based on good analysis of the interpretations. • The student's explanation is fully backed up in an effective way.
1	1–2	• The student has written a simple valid explanation but there is only limited analysis. • Some support to back up the reason is given, but this support is not linked very well to the explanation.
	0	No rewardable content.

2 Use the mark scheme below to assign a mark to each answer. Explain your decisions.

I would award Answer 1 .... out of 4 marks because ....

....

....

I would award Answer 2 .... out of 4 marks because ....

....

....

I would award Answer 3 .... out of 4 marks because ....

....

....

Improve the answer

1 Write an improved answer to the question below about Interpretations 1 and 2 on page 75.
Use the hints to make sure your answer is awarded 4 marks.

---

3 (c) Suggest **one** reason why Interpretations 1 and 2 give different views about the ways that Hitler undermined democracy in Germany in 1933–34.
You may use Sources E and F on page 74 to help explain your answer. (4)

Had a go

One reason why the interpretations are different could be that they are based on different sources. For example, Source E supports Interpretation 1 more than Interpretation 2.

> **Hints**
> - Analyse the interpretations to explain why they are different. You only need to give **one** reason.
> - Back up your explanations with details from the interpretations, sources and/or your own knowledge.

....

....

....

....

....

....

....

....

....

....

> Remember that there are several different reasons why interpretations might be different from each other, like using sources differently or having a different focus.

2 Use the same hints to improve this next answer to the same question, so that it would be awarded 4 marks.

Had a go

One reason why the interpretations have different views could be that one is focusing on the Reichstag fire while the other is about the Reichstag fire decree.

....

....

....

....

....

....

....

Re-order the answer

1 A student has written a plan to answer the question below. Decide which of their points support Interpretation 1 on page 75, and which counter it. Mark each with an S (support) or a C (counter). One has been done for you.

> In deciding 'How far do you agree?' for Question 3(d), you should consider points that support the interpretation and points that do not support (counter) the interpretation, then use this to reach your overall judgement.

3   (d)   How far do you agree with Interpretation 1 about the ways that Hitler undermined democracy in Germany in 1933–34?
Explain your answer, using both interpretations and your knowledge of the historical context.

(Total for Question 3(d) = 16 marks + 4 SPaG marks)

[S]   Interpretation 1 suggests that the measures that Hitler used to undermine democracy were not 'carefully planned and coordinated' but were instead unplanned and 'largely irrational'.

[ ]   Interpretation 1 suggests that it was fear of a communist uprising that made Hitler get the Reichstag fire decree approved and then use it to arrest thousands of communists.

[ ]   Interpretation 2 suggests that many ordinary Germans also believed that a communist uprising was very likely to take place, and were anxious to see communists arrested.

[ ]   Hitler was able to use the Reichstag Fire to put pressure on Hindenburg into signing the Reichstag fire decree and also to call an election for 5 March. Hindenburg disliked Hitler and might not have been persuaded if the Nazis were behaving in a 'largely irrational' way.

[ ]   Despite the effective campaigning described in Interpretation 2, the Nazis did not win an absolute majority in the March 1933 election. This was a failure for Hitler, which could suggest that he had seized an opportunity with the Reichstag Fire rather than working to a long-term, carefully thought-out plan.

[ ]   The main way that Hitler overturned democracy was through the Enabling Act. This was a carefully planned and coordinated Act that the Nazis had been working towards. Therefore, even if their first responses after the Reichstag Fire had been uncoordinated, Hitler knew exactly what he wanted to do in the longer term.

> Question 3(d) is worth 16 marks, plus another 4 marks for SPaG, so I tried to leave plenty of time to tackle this question properly.

Mark the answer

1 Draw lines to connect the marker's comments about SPaG to the relevant parts of the answer below about Interpretation 1 on page 75. One has been done for you.

3 (d) How far do you agree with Interpretation 1 about the ways that Hitler undermined democracy in Germany in 1933–34?
Explain your answer, using both interpretations and your knowledge of the historical context.

(Total for Question 3(d) = 16 marks + 4 SPaG marks)

I do agree with 1 because it say that Hitler and the nazis we

not working to a definit plan but were afriad of a comunists'

uprising. because of unemployment in Weimar Germany the

comunists' party called the KPD was getting more powerful

so in March 1932 for instance the KPD candidate got

14 percent for president even though Hitler got 30 percent

so it wasnt the unemployed voting for Hitler so much as for

the KPD. ordinary middle class people were very worried

by comunists' violence because of fighting in the streets

between the RFB (red front Fighters) and the SA and other

types of comunists' violence and this is what interpretation

2 shows when it says about people beliving about a

communits' plot and they belived that the comunists' had

started the Reichstag Fire. So I'm arguing there was a lot of

fear in Germany about a comunists' uprising, like 1 says.

> The student has made numerous spelling mistakes but it is still reasonably clear what the student is arguing here.

> Punctuation is reasonably accurate in this sentence, but in the rest of the paragraph there are errors, especially with capitalisation.

> Good use of some specialist terms, used appropriately to describe violence with the SA.

> Grammar is not always accurate in this section, which makes the student's point quite hard to follow.

2 Use the mark scheme below to assign a mark to the answer. Explain your decision. There are 4 marks available for SPaG.

Performance	Mark	Descriptor
High	4	Spelling and punctuation is used with a consistent level of accuracy. A wide range of specialist terms are also used as appropriate.
Intermediate	2–3	Spelling and punctuation is used with a considerable level of accuracy. A good range of specialist terms are also used as appropriate.
Threshold	1	Spelling and punctuation is used with a reasonable level of accuracy. Grammar errors sometimes make it difficult to follow the answer. A limited range of specialist terms are used appropriately.
	0	Errors in spelling, punctuation and grammar make it very difficult to understand the answer.

I would award this answer .... out of 4 marks because ....

....

....

....

Complete the answer

1 Use the prompts to complete the student's answer below about Interpretation 1 on page 75.

3 (d) How far do you agree with Interpretation 1 about the ways that Hitler undermined democracy in Germany in 1933–34?
Explain your answer, using both interpretations and your knowledge of the historical context.

(Total for Question 3(d) = 16 marks + 4 SPaG marks)

Interpretation 1 suggests that Hitler and the Nazis were panicked into unplanned
responses to the Reichstag Fire because of their fear of a communist uprising. This
interpretation is supported by ....
....
....
....
....
....
....
....
....
....
....

However, there are also points against this interpretation. For example, ...
....
....
....
....
....
....
....
....
....
....
....
....
....
....

Sources E and F

Source E: From the **memoirs** of Rudolf Diels, Head of the Prussian Police, published in 1950. Diels was responsible for questioning Marinus van der Lubbe*. Here he recalls Hitler's reaction to the Reichstag Fire in 1933.

> Hitler… started screaming at the top of his voice. 'Now we'll show them! The German people have been
>
> soft too long. Every Communist official must be shot. All Communist deputies must be hanged tonight. All
>
> friends of the Communists must be locked up. And that goes for the Social Democrats too.'

* Van der Lubbe was the Dutch communist found by police inside the burning Reichstag building. He was found guilty of starting the fire.

Source F: From a statement by General Halder, Chief of the German General Staff to the Nuremburg War Crimes Trial (1945). Halder had been asked about the Reichstag Fire.

> At a luncheon on the birthday of the Führer in 1942 the conversation turned to the Reichstag Fire. I heard
>
> with my own ears when Göring interrupted the conversation and shouted: 'The only one who really knows
>
> about the Reichstag building is I, because I set it on fire.'

Interpretations 1 and 2

Interpretation 1: From *Nazism 1919–1945* by J. Noakes and G. Pridham, published in 1998.

Whoever was responsible [for the Reichstag Fire], the Nazis exploited their opportunity to the full. Yet it appears the measures which followed were not carefully planned and coordinated but were rather spontaneous and largely irrational responses to an imagined threat of a Communist uprising. … In fact, the Nazis had hoped to postpone the elimination of the Communists until after the election when they would be in a stronger position to deal with them. But their fear of an uprising prompted them to take precipitate [unplanned, hasty] and drastic action.

Interpretation 2: From *The Coming of the Third Reich* by R. Evans, published in 2004.

The Reichstag fire decree* was launched amidst a barrage of propaganda in which Göring and the Nazi leadership painted a drastic picture of an imminent 'German Bolshevik Revolution' accompanied by outrages and atrocities of every kind. The propaganda had its effect. Ordinary middle-class citizens… shuddered to think of the fate that Germany had so narrowly escaped, and were impressed by the proofs of the dastardly Communist plot that Göring provided… Some local Nazi authorities expressed their fear that public disorder would occur if the culprits were not immediately executed.

* The Reichstag fire decree was issued by Hindenburg immediately after the Reichstag Fire, once Hitler had convinced him that the fire was the start of a communist uprising. The decree took away many rights from the German people.

Where an example answer is given, this is not necessarily the only correct response. In most cases, there is a range of responses that can gain full marks.

In questions that have more than one correct answer, you will see the (Suggested answer) stamp.

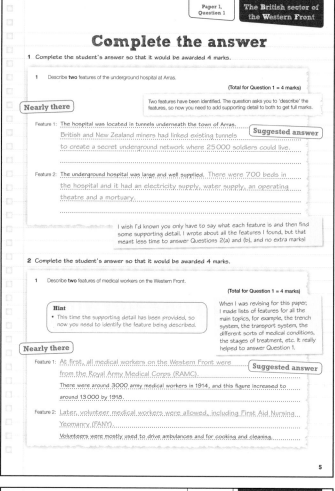

Paper 1, Question 1 | The British sector of the Western Front

Complete the answer

1 Complete the student's answer so that it would be awarded 4 marks.

1 Describe **two** features of the underground hospital at Arras.

(Total for Question 1 = 4 marks)

Nearly there

Two features have been identified. The question asks you to 'describe' the features, so now you need to add supporting detail to both to get full marks.

Feature 1: The hospital was located in tunnels underneath the town of Arras. British and New Zealand miners had linked existing tunnels to create a secret underground network where 25 000 soldiers could live.   **Suggested answer**

Feature 2: The underground hospital was large and well supplied. There were 700 beds in the hospital and it had an electricity supply, water supply, an operating theatre and a mortuary.

I wish I'd known you only have to say what each feature is and then find some supporting detail. I wrote about all the features I found, but that meant less time to answer Questions 2(a) and (b), and no extra marks!

2 Complete the student's answer so that it would be awarded 4 marks.

1 Describe **two** features of medical workers on the Western Front.

(Total for Question 1 = 4 marks)

Hint
• This time the supporting detail has been provided, so now you need to identify the feature being described.

When I was revising for this paper, I made lists of features for all the main topics, for example, the trench system, the transport system, the different sorts of medical conditions, the stages of treatment, etc. It really helped to answer Question 1.

Nearly there

Feature 1: At first, all medical workers on the Western Front were from the Royal Army Medical Corps (RAMC).   **Suggested answer**
There were around 3000 army medical workers in 1914, and this figure increased to around 13 000 by 1918.

Feature 2: Later, volunteer medical workers were allowed, including First Aid Nursing Yeomanry (FANY).
Volunteers were mostly used to drive ambulances and for cooking and cleaning.

5

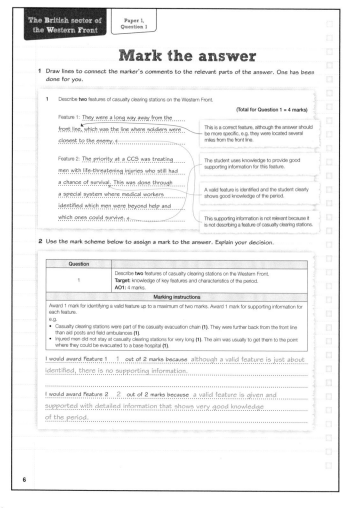

The British sector of the Western Front | Paper 1, Question 1

Mark the answer

1 Draw lines to connect the marker's comments to the relevant parts of the answer. One has been done for you.

1 Describe **two** features of casualty clearing stations on the Western Front.

(Total for Question 1 = 4 marks)

Feature 1: They were a long way away from the front line, which was the line where soldiers were closest to the enemy.

This is a correct feature, although the answer should be more specific, e.g. they were located several miles from the front line.

Feature 2: The priority at a CCS was treating men with life-threatening injuries who still had a chance of survival. This was done through a special system where medical workers identified which men were beyond help and which ones could survive.

The student uses knowledge to provide good supporting information for this feature.

A valid feature is identified and the student clearly shows good knowledge of the period.

This supporting information is not relevant because it is not describing a feature of casualty clearing stations.

2 Use the mark scheme below to assign a mark to the answer. Explain your decision.

Question	
1	Describe **two** features of casualty clearing stations on the Western Front. **Target:** knowledge of key features and characteristics of the period. AO1: 4 marks.
	Marking instructions

Award 1 mark for identifying a valid feature up to a maximum of two marks. Award 1 mark for supporting information for each feature.
e.g.
• Casualty clearing stations were part of the casualty evacuation chain **(1)**. They were further back from the front line than aid posts and field ambulances **(1)**.
• Injured men did not stay at casualty clearing stations for very long **(1)**. The aim was usually to get them to the point where they could be evacuated to a base hospital **(1)**.

I would award Feature 1   1   out of 2 marks because although a valid feature is just about identified, there is no supporting information.

I would award Feature 2   2   out of 2 marks because a valid feature is given and supported with detailed information that shows very good knowledge of the period.

6

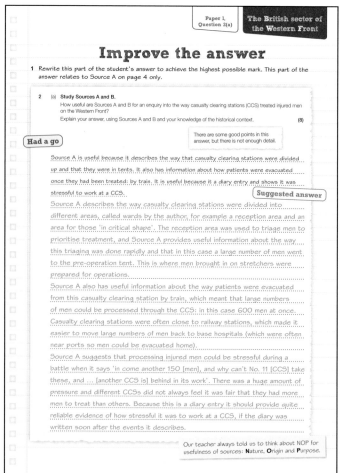

Paper 1, Question 2(a) | The British sector of the Western Front

Improve the answer

1 Rewrite this part of the student's answer to achieve the highest possible mark. This part of the answer relates to Source A on page 4 only.

2 (a) Study Sources A and B.
How useful are Sources A and B for an enquiry into the way casualty clearing stations (CCS) treated injured men on the Western Front?
Explain your answer, using Sources A and B and your knowledge of the historical context.   (8)

Had a go

There are some good points in this answer, but there is not enough detail.

Source A is useful because it describes the way that casualty clearing stations were divided up and that they were in tents. It also has information about how patients were evacuated once they had been treated: by train. It is useful because it a diary entry and shows it was stressful to work at a CCS.   **Suggested answer**
Source A describes the way casualty clearing stations were divided into different areas, called wards by the author, for example a reception area and an area for those 'in critical shape'. The reception area was used to triage men to prioritise treatment, and Source A provides useful information about the way this triaging was done rapidly and that in this case a large number of men went to the pre-operation tent. This is where men brought in on stretchers were prepared for operations.
Source A also has useful information about the way patients were evacuated from this casualty clearing station by train, which meant that large numbers of men could be processed through the CCS: in this case 600 men at once. Casualty clearing stations were often close to railway stations, which made it easier to move large numbers of men back to base hospitals (which were often near ports so men could be evacuated home).
Source A suggests that processing injured men could be stressful during a battle when it says 'in come another 150 [men], and why can't No. 11 [CCS] take these, and ... [another CCS is] behind in its work'. There is a huge amount of pressure and different CCSs did not always feel it was fair that they had more men to treat than others. Because this is a diary entry it should provide quite reliable evidence of how stressful it was to work at a CCS, if the diary was written soon after the events it describes.

Our teacher always told us to think about NOP for usefulness of sources: Nature, Origin and Purpose.

7

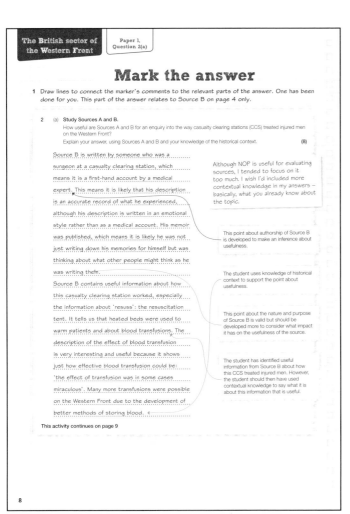

The British sector of the Western Front — Paper 1, Question 2(a)

Mark the answer

1 Draw lines to connect the marker's comments to the relevant parts of the answer. One has been done for you. This part of the answer relates to Source B on page 4 only.

2 (a) Study Sources A and B.
How useful are Sources A and B for an enquiry into the way casualty clearing stations (CCS) treated injured men on the Western Front?
Explain your answer, using Sources A and B and your knowledge of the historical context. (8)

Source B is written by someone who was a surgeon at a casualty clearing station, which means it is a first-hand account by a medical expert. This means it is likely that his description is an accurate record of what he experienced, although his description is written in an emotional style rather than as a medical account. His memoir was published, which means it is likely he was not just writing down his memories for himself but was thinking about what other people might think as he was writing them.

Source B contains useful information about how this casualty clearing station worked, especially the information about 'resuss': the resuscitation tent. It tells us that heated beds were used to warm patients and about blood transfusions. The description of the effect of blood transfusion is very interesting and useful because it shows just how effective blood transfusion could be: 'the effect of transfusion was in some cases miraculous'. Many more transfusions were possible on the Western Front due to the development of better methods of storing blood.

Although NOP is useful for evaluating sources, I tended to focus on it too much. I wish I'd included more contextual knowledge in my answers – basically, what you already know about the topic.

This point about authorship of Source B is developed to make an inference about usefulness.

The student uses knowledge of historical context to support the point about usefulness.

This point about the nature and purpose of Source B is valid but should be developed more to consider what impact it has on the usefulness of the source.

The student has identified useful information from Source B about how this CCS treated injured men. However, the student should then have used contextual knowledge to say what it is about this information that is useful.

This activity continues on page 9

8

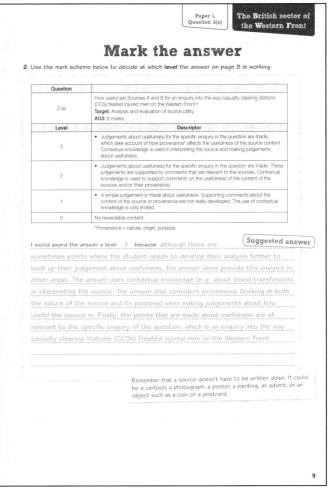

The British sector of the Western Front — Paper 1, Question 2(a)

Mark the answer

2 Use the mark scheme below to decide at which **level** the answer on page 8 is working.

Question	
2 (a)	How useful are Sources A and B for an enquiry into the way casualty clearing stations (CCS) treated injured men on the Western Front? **Target:** Analysis and evaluation of source utility. **AO3:** 8 marks.

Level	Descriptor
3	• Judgements about usefulness for the specific enquiry in the question are made, which take account of how provenance* affects the usefulness of the source content. Contextual knowledge is used in interpreting the source and making judgements about usefulness.
2	• Judgements about usefulness for the specific enquiry in the question are made. These judgements are supported by comments that are relevant to the sources. Contextual knowledge is used to support comments on the usefulness of the content of the sources and/or their provenance.
1	• A simple judgement is made about usefulness. Supporting comments about the content of the source or provenance are not really developed. The use of contextual knowledge is only limited.
0	No rewardable content.

*Provenance = nature, origin, purpose.

I would award the answer a level **3** because although there are sometimes points where the student needs to develop their analysis further to back up their judgement about usefulness, the answer does provide this analysis in other areas. The answer uses contextual knowledge (e.g. about blood transfusions) in interpreting the source. The answer also considers provenance (looking at both the nature of the source and its purpose) when making judgements about how useful the source is. Finally, the points that are made about usefulness are all relevant to the specific enquiry of the question, which is an enquiry into the way casualty clearing stations (CCSs) treated injured men on the Western Front.

Suggested answer

Remember that a source doesn't have to be written down. It could be a cartoon, a photograph, a poster, a painting, an advert, or an object such as a coin or a postcard.

9

The British sector of the Western Front — Paper 1, Question 2(b)

Find the answer

1 Use the marking instructions below to find the answer that would **not** be awarded the mark.

2 (b) Study Source B.
How could you follow up Source B to find out more about the way casualty clearing stations treated injured men on the Western Front? (4)

Detail in Source B that I would follow up:

A 'The effect of transfusion was in some cases miraculous.'

B '"Resuss" was a dreadful place.'

C 'an equally rapid evacuation takes place'

D 'the warming-up under cradles in heated beds'

When you are picking the source detail you are going to use, sense-check that you can use it to answer all four parts of Question 2(b).

Marking instructions
Award 1 mark for choosing a detail in Source B that could be developed into a follow-up enquiry.

Answer **C** would not get the mark because it comes from Source A, not from Source B.

2 Look at this student's answer to the first part of the question.

Detail in Source B that I would follow up: 'The effect of transfusion was in some cases miraculous.'

Use the marking instructions to find the answer that would best link to this detail.

Question I would ask:

A Why did some soldiers need blood transfusions but not others?

B Were blood transfusions a new treatment?

C Did soldiers mind having blood transfusions?

D How often did casualty clearing stations use blood transfusions?

Marking instructions
Award 1 mark for a question which is linked to the detail in Source B that could form the basis of a follow-up enquiry.

Answer **D** would get the mark because it is the answer that has the clearest link to the enquiry, which is about the way that casualty clearing stations worked.

10

The British sector of the Western Front — Paper 1, Question 2(b)

Find the answer

1 Another student has answered the first two parts of a 2(b) question.

Detail in Source B that I would follow up: 'The effect of transfusion was in some cases miraculous.'
Question I would ask: How much blood did casualty clearing stations have stored for transfusions?

Use the marking instructions to find the best source to use to link to the above answers.

What type of source I could use:

A Army medical records about the amount of blood available to casualty clearing stations

B Newspaper reports about men who recovered after having blood transfusions

C Photographs of casualty clearing stations in action

Marking instructions
Award 1 mark for identifying an appropriate source to help answer the selected question.

Answer **A** would get the mark because this source is most likely to record facts and figures about how much blood was stored.

2 Another student has written the following answers to part of a 2(b) question.

Question I would ask: What problems occurred with blood transfusions at casualty clearing stations?
What type of source I could use: Letters home by medical workers

Use the marking instructions to find the answer that would **not** be awarded the mark.

How this might help answer my question:

A The letters might record experiences of transfusions that went wrong.

B They might show that medical workers found transfusions difficult.

C The letters home might include graphs of the numbers of unsuccessful blood transfusion.

Marking instructions
Award 1 mark for a response that shows how the source could help answer the selected question.

Answer **C** would not get the mark because it is unlikely that letters home would include statistical information like this, which is more likely to be found in army medical records.

11

Answers

Mark the answer

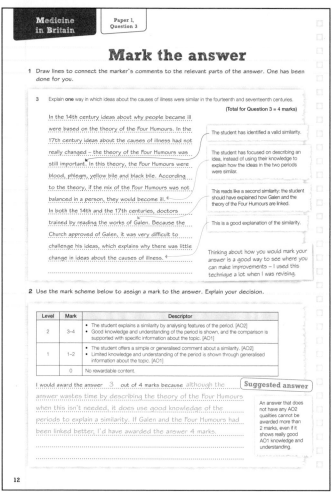

1 Draw lines to connect the marker's comments to the relevant parts of the answer. One has been done for you.

3 Explain **one** way in which ideas about the causes of illness were similar in the fourteenth and seventeenth centuries.

(Total for Question 3 = 4 marks)

In the 14th century ideas about why people became ill were based on the theory of the Four Humours. In the 17th century ideas about the causes of illness had not really changed – the theory of the Four Humours was still important. In this theory, the Four Humours were blood, phlegm, yellow bile and black bile. According to the theory, if the mix of the Four Humours was not balanced in a person, they would become ill. In both the 14th and the 17th centuries, doctors trained by reading the works of Galen. Because the Church approved of Galen, it was very difficult to challenge his ideas, which explains why there was little change in ideas about the causes of illness.

The student has identified a valid similarity.

The student has focused on describing an idea, instead of using their knowledge to explain how the ideas in the two periods were similar.

This reads like a second similarity: the student should have explained how Galen and the theory of the Four Humours are linked.

This is a good explanation of the similarity.

Thinking about how you would mark your answer is a good way to see where you can make improvements – I used this technique a lot when I was revising.

2 Use the mark scheme below to assign a mark to the answer. Explain your decision.

Level	Mark	Descriptor
2	3–4	• The student explains a similarity by analysing features of the period. [AO2] • Good knowledge and understanding of the period is shown, and the comparison is supported with specific information about the topic. [AO1]
1	1–2	• The student offers a simple or generalised comment about a similarity. [AO2] • Limited knowledge and understanding of the period is shown through generalised information about the topic. [AO1]
	0	No rewardable content.

I would award the answer **3** out of 4 marks because *although the* **Suggested answer** *answer wastes time by describing the theory of the Four Humours when this isn't needed, it does use good knowledge of the periods to explain a similarity. If Galen and the Four Humours had been linked better, I'd have awarded the answer 4 marks.*

An answer that does not have any AO2 qualities cannot be awarded more than 2 marks, even if it shows really good AO1 knowledge and understanding.

12

Improve the answer

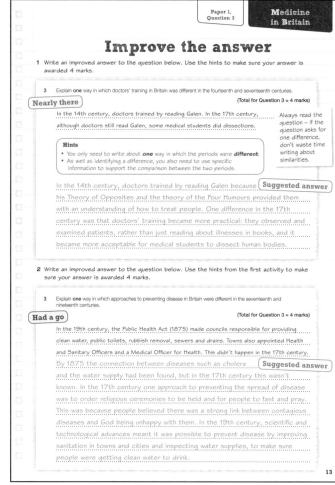

1 Write an improved answer to the question below. Use the hints to make sure your answer is awarded 4 marks.

3 Explain **one** way in which doctors' training in Britain was different in the fourteenth and seventeenth centuries.

(Total for Question 3 = 4 marks)

Nearly there

In the 14th century, doctors trained by reading Galen. In the 17th century, although doctors still read Galen, some medical students did dissections.

Always read the question – if the question asks for one difference, don't waste time writing about similarities.

Hints
• You only need to write about **one** way in which the periods were **different**.
• As well as identifying a difference, you also need to use specific information to support the comparison between the two periods.

In the 14th century, doctors trained by reading Galen because **Suggested answer** his Theory of Opposites and the theory of the Four Humours provided them with an understanding of how to treat people. One difference in the 17th century was that doctors' training became more practical: they observed and examined patients, rather than just reading about illnesses in books, and it became more acceptable for medical students to dissect human bodies.

2 Write an improved answer to the question below. Use the hints from the first activity to make sure your answer is awarded 4 marks.

3 Explain **one** way in which approaches to preventing disease in Britain were different in the seventeenth and nineteenth centuries.

Had a go

(Total for Question 3 = 4 marks)

In the 19th century, the Public Health Act (1875) made councils responsible for providing clean water, public toilets, rubbish removal, sewers and drains. Towns also appointed Health and Sanitary Officers and a Medical Officer for Health. This didn't happen in the 17th century. By 1875 the connection between diseases such as cholera **Suggested answer** and the water supply had been found, but in the 17th century this wasn't known. In the 17th century one approach to preventing the spread of disease was to order religious ceremonies to be held and for people to fast and pray. This was because people believed there was a strong link between contagious diseases and God being unhappy with them. In the 19th century, scientific and technological advances meant it was possible to prevent disease by improving sanitation in towns and cities and inspecting water supplies, to make sure people were getting clean water to drink.

13

Complete the answer

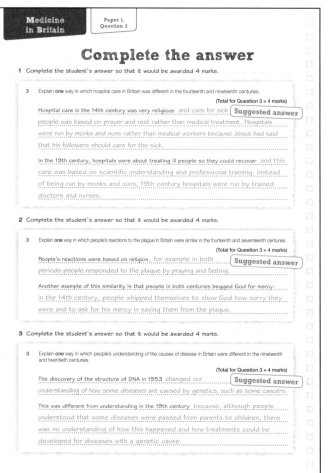

1 Complete the student's answer so that it would be awarded 4 marks.

3 Explain **one** way in which hospital care in Britain was different in the fourteenth and nineteenth centuries.

(Total for Question 3 = 4 marks)

Hospital care in the 14th century was very religious *and care for sick* **Suggested answer** *people was based on prayer and rest rather than medical treatment. Hospitals were run by monks and nuns rather than medical workers because Jesus had said that his followers should care for the sick.*

In the 19th century, hospitals were about treating ill people so they could recover *and this care was based on scientific understanding and professional training. Instead of being run by monks and nuns, 19th century hospitals were run by trained doctors and nurses.*

2 Complete the student's answer so that it would be awarded 4 marks.

3 Explain **one** way in which people's reactions to the plague in Britain were similar in the fourteenth and seventeenth centuries.

(Total for Question 3 = 4 marks)

People's reactions were based on religion, *for example in both* **Suggested answer** *periods people responded to the plague by praying and fasting.*

Another example of this similarity is that people in both centuries begged God for mercy*: in the 14th century, people whipped themselves to show God how sorry they were and to ask for his mercy in saving them from the plague.*

3 Complete the student's answer so that it would be awarded 4 marks.

3 Explain **one** way in which people's understanding of the causes of disease in Britain were different in the nineteenth and twentieth centuries.

(Total for Question 3 = 4 marks)

The discovery of the structure of DNA in 1953 *changed our* **Suggested answer** *understanding of how some diseases are caused by genetics, such as some cancers.*

This was different from understanding in the 19th century *because, although people understood that some diseases were passed from parents to children, there was no understanding of how this happened and how treatments could be developed for diseases with a genetic cause.*

14

Find the answer

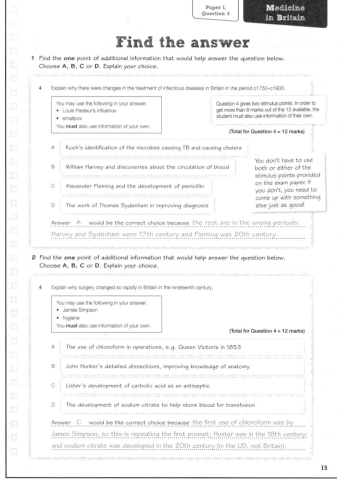

1 Find the **one** point of additional information that would help answer the question below. Choose **A, B, C** or **D**. Explain your choice.

4 Explain why there were changes in the treatment of infectious diseases in Britain in the period c1750–c1900.

You may use the following in your answer:
• Louis Pasteur's influence
• smallpox
You **must** also use information of your own.

Question 4 gives two stimulus points. In order to get more than 8 marks out of the 12 available, the student must also use information of their own.

(Total for Question 4 = 12 marks)

A	Koch's identification of the microbes causing TB and causing cholera
B	William Harvey and discoveries about the circulation of blood
C	Alexander Fleming and the development of penicillin
D	The work of Thomas Sydenham in improving diagnosis

You don't have to use both or either of the stimulus points provided on the exam paper. If you don't, you need to come up with something else just as good!

Answer **A** would be the correct choice because *the rest are in the wrong periods: Harvey and Sydenham were 17th century and Fleming was 20th century.*

2 Find the **one** point of additional information that would help answer the question below. Choose **A, B, C** or **D**. Explain your choice.

4 Explain why surgery changed so rapidly in Britain in the nineteenth century.

You may use the following in your answer:
• James Simpson
• hygiene
You **must** also use information of your own.

(Total for Question 4 = 12 marks)

A	The use of chloroform in operations, e.g. Queen Victoria in 1853
B	John Hunter's detailed dissections, improving knowledge of anatomy
C	Lister's development of carbolic acid as an antiseptic
D	The development of sodium citrate to help store blood for transfusion

Answer **C** would be the correct choice because *the first use of chloroform was by James Simpson, so this is repeating the first prompt; Hunter was in the 18th century; and sodium citrate was developed in the 20th century (in the US, not Britain).*

15

Medicine in Britain — Paper 1, Question 4

Improve the answer

1 Write an improved answer to the question below. Use the hints to make sure your answer achieves the highest possible mark.

4 Explain why there were changes in the treatment of infectious diseases in Britain in the period c1800–c1900.

You may use the following in your answer:
- Louis Pasteur's influence
- smallpox
You **must** also use information of your own.

(Total for Question 4 = 12 marks)

Had a go

Jenner developed vaccination just before the 19th century began. He noticed that people who had had cowpox didn't get smallpox. Jenner's experiments with inoculating people with cowpox and then smallpox showed that this method, known as vaccination, could prevent people from catching a disease. Louis Pasteur identified that decay was caused by microbes in the air.

Hints
- **Explain** the change, don't just **describe** it. Why did these factors cause change?
- You need to add information of your own to access the highest marks.
- Remember to link your points together in longer answers.

Suggested answer

Throughout the 19th century there were important developments in understanding what caused disease and how to treat it. Sometimes the treatment came before the understanding. This was true for Jenner and the development of vaccination. By careful experimentation, Jenner proved that inoculating people with cowpox often prevented them from catching smallpox, but was unable to explain why. Nevertheless, in the 19th century the British government promoted his vaccination treatment. There was a rapid reduction in smallpox deaths. Vaccination was linked to growing evidence that disease was not caused by miasma, the main theory about infectious disease before the 19th century. For example, John Snow advised boiling water before drinking as a way of preventing the spread of diseases such as cholera. Louis Pasteur's work in France provided scientific proof for germs (microbes) being responsible for diseases; Koch in Germany then identified the specific microbes causing anthrax, TB and cholera. Scientists used his methods to discover the specific microbes that caused other diseases, such as typhus and bubonic plague. This made it possible to develop vaccinations for specific diseases. The communication of scientific discoveries through medical journals was very important in the development of new treatments.

16

Medicine in Britain — Paper 1, Question 4

Complete the answer

1 Complete the student's answer to achieve the highest possible mark.

4 Explain why surgery changed so rapidly in the nineteenth century.

You may use the following in your answer:
- James Simpson
- hygiene
You **must** also use information of your own.

Make sure that your answers are relevant; only write about the period asked about in the question.

(Total for Question 4 = 12 marks)

Hint
- Focus on **change** – explain **why** the 19th century was different from previous periods.

The discovery of anaesthetics was a major breakthrough in surgery because **Suggested answer** it meant that surgeons did not have to work quickly to minimise pain and shock, and could do more complicated internal operations. Although early anaesthetics had problems, James Simpson's development of chloroform and John Snow's invention of a chloroform inhaler were important in making them safer. In 1853, Queen Victoria used chloroform during childbirth, convincing other surgeons and patients that the benefits of anaesthetics outweighed the risks, and the impact of chloroform on surgery increased.

Infection limited the impact of anaesthetics because although operations could now take longer, operating conditions were unhygienic so patients died of sepsis. Some medical workers found that better hygiene reduced the death rate for patients. For example, Florence Nightingale insisted on clean wards and one patient per bed. Before Pasteur's germ theory, however, medical workers did not understand why hygiene helped combat infection. They thought it stopped miasma, which led to techniques such as keeping wounds tightly bound. This in fact created better conditions for bacteria to grow.

Although there was opposition to Lister's work at first, his ideas led to major changes in surgery because surgeons who used his techniques saw big reductions in the numbers of patients dying from infection. In 1878, Koch identified the microbe causing blood poisoning, convincing surgeons to use antiseptic treatments.

These developments contributed to rapid change in surgery in the 19th century because they revolutionised what surgeons could do: anaesthetics allowed surgeons to attempt internal operations and antiseptics meant that more people recovered from them, encouraging more surgeons to attempt them. Significant problems such as the problem of blood loss still remained. However, surgery at the end of the 19th century had advanced very rapidly since the start.

17

Medicine in Britain — Paper 1, Question 5

Re-order the answer

1 A student has written a plan to answer this question. Decide which of their points support the statement below and which counter it. Mark each with an S (support) or a C (counter). One has been done for you.

5 'Religion was the main reason why medical treatment made little progress in Britain during the period c1500–c1800.' How far do you agree? Explain your answer.

You may use the following in your answer:
- the Great Plague
- the influence of Vesalius
You **must** also use information of your own.

Questions 5 and 6 ask 'how far you agree' with a statement. This involves making points that support the statement and points that go against it, and then making a judgement about how far the evidence supports the statement.

(Total for Question 5 = 16 marks + 4 SPaG marks)

S	In the Great Plague, people turned to prayer and fasting to protect them from infection.
C	Vesalius's work showed that Galen had been wrong about some important things. The Church approved of Galen.
S	People in the 16th century still believed that the king's touch could cure some diseases because they thought the king was chosen by God.
S	The Church continued to discourage dissection in the 16th century, and most doctors did not challenge this.
C	People responded to the Great Plague in very similar ways to the Black Death: evidence of continuity.
C	Not all responses were religious: William Harvey and scientific approach led to new understanding of how the body worked. However, this took time to influence medical treatment.
C	Reformation – more than one Church; Renaissance – people wanting to find things out for themselves through experiment rather than just listening to what the Church said.
C	Doctors also held on to mistaken scientific ideas, for example the miasma theory about the causes of illness and disease.

Question 5 is worth 16 marks, plus another 4 for SPaG, so I tried to leave plenty of time to answer it properly.

18

Medicine in Britain — Paper 1, Question 5

Mark the answer

1 Draw lines to connect the marker's comments about SPaG to the relevant parts of the answer. One has been done for you.

5 'Religion was the main reason why medical treatment made little progress in Britain during the period c1500–c1800.' How far do you agree? Explain your answer.

You may use the following in your answer:
- the Great Plague
- the influence of Vesalius
You **must** also use information of your own.

Questions 5 and 6 each have 4 marks available for Spelling, Punctuation and Grammar (SPaG) and the use of 'specialist terminology'. This means that you should use proper historical terms.

(Total for Question 5 = 16 marks + 4 SPaG marks)

People in the 15th century and in the 17th century both though that religion was very important. It is true medicine did not make much progress this period. for example, there were epidemics of plagues in both centuries, but peoples understanding of what caused plague and how they should be treated staid the same or nearly. people believed in God being not pleased with people for a cause and prayer and fasting for a treatment. Another similarity that had religion connetions Galen was important still. Galens theory was supported by the church. the church did not want anyone to challenge. What it said was true about religion and the same for medicine causes and treatments.

There are spelling mistakes but these do not get in the way of understanding what the student means to say.

Punctuation is reasonably accurate in this paragraph but there are errors that do make the student's meaning harder to follow.

Good use of some specialist terms, used appropriately, for example epidemic, plague, fasting, prayer, treatment.

Grammar is not always accurate in this section, although the meaning is generally clear.

2 Use the mark scheme below to assign a mark to the answer. There are 4 marks available for SPaG.

Performance	Mark	Descriptor
High	4	Spelling and punctuation is used with a consistent level of accuracy. A wide range of specialist terms are also used as appropriate.
Intermediate	2–3	Spelling and punctuation is used with a considerable level of accuracy. A good range of specialist terms are also used as appropriate.
Threshold	1	Spelling and punctuation is used with a reasonable level of accuracy. Grammar errors sometimes make it difficult to follow the answer. A limited range of specialist terms are used appropriately.
	0	Errors in spelling, punctuation and grammar make it very difficult to understand the answer.

I would give this answer 1 out of 4 marks because the spelling, punctuation **Suggested answer** and grammar are only reasonably accurate, which means it's sometimes hard to understand the answer. The student uses some specialist terms but not enough for a higher mark.

19

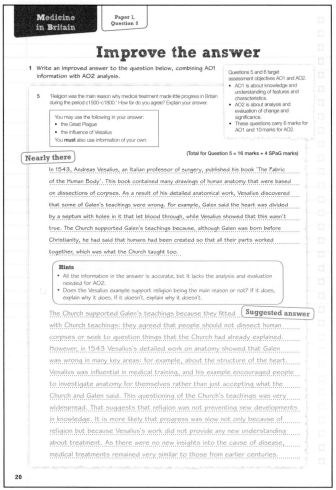

Medicine in Britain — Paper 1, Question 5

Improve the answer

1 Write an improved answer to the question below, combining AO1 information with AO2 analysis.

> Questions 5 and 6 target assessment objectives AO1 and AO2.
> * AO1 is about knowledge and understanding of features and characteristics.
> * AO2 is about analysis and evaluation of change and significance.
> * These questions carry 6 marks for AO1 and 10 marks for AO2.

5 'Religion was the main reason why medical treatment made little progress in Britain during the period c1500–c1800.' How far do you agree? Explain your answer.

You may use the following in your answer:
* the Great Plague
* the influence of Vesalius
You **must** also use information of your own.

(Total for Question 5 = 16 marks + 4 SPaG marks)

Nearly there

In 1543, Andreas Vesalius, an Italian professor of surgery, published his book 'The Fabric of the Human Body'. This book contained many drawings of human anatomy that were based on dissections of corpses. As a result of his detailed anatomical work, Vesalius discovered that some of Galen's teachings were wrong. For example, Galen said the heart was divided by a septum with holes in it that let blood through, while Vesalius showed that this wasn't true. The Church supported Galen's teachings because, although Galen was born before Christianity, he had said that humans had been created so that all their parts worked together, which was what the Church taught too.

Hints
* All the information in the answer is accurate, but it lacks the analysis and evaluation needed for AO2.
* Does the Vesalius example support religion being the main reason or not? If it does, explain why it does. If it doesn't, explain why it doesn't.

Suggested answer

The Church supported Galen's teachings because they fitted with Church teachings: they agreed that people should not dissect human corpses or seek to question things that the Church had already explained. However, in 1543 Vesalius's detailed work on anatomy showed that Galen was wrong in many key areas: for example, about the structure of the heart. Vesalius was influential in medical training, and his example encouraged people to investigate anatomy for themselves rather than just accepting what the Church and Galen said. This questioning of the Church's teachings was very widespread. That suggests that religion was not preventing new developments in knowledge. It is more likely that progress was slow not only because of religion but because Vesalius's work did not provide any new understanding about treatment. As there were no new insights into the cause of disease, medical treatments remained very similar to those from earlier centuries.

20

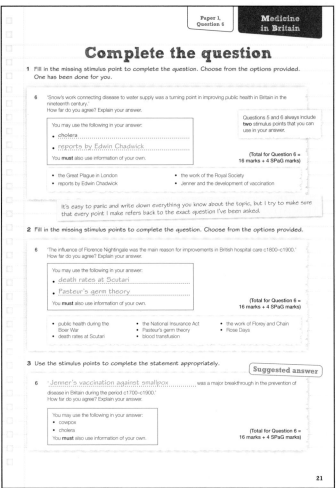

Paper 1, Question 6 — **Medicine in Britain**

Complete the question

1 Fill in the missing stimulus point to complete the question. Choose from the options provided. One has been done for you.

6 'Snow's work connecting disease to water supply was a turning point in improving public health in Britain in the nineteenth century.' How far do you agree? Explain your answer.

You may use the following in your answer:
* cholera
* reports by Edwin Chadwick
You **must** also use information of your own.

> Questions 5 and 6 always include **two** stimulus points that you can use in your answer.

(Total for Question 6 = 16 marks + 4 SPaG marks)

* the Great Plague in London
* reports by Edwin Chadwick
* the work of the Royal Society
* Jenner and the development of vaccination

> It's easy to panic and write down everything you know about the topic, but I try to make sure that every point I make refers back to the exact question I've been asked.

2 Fill in the missing stimulus points to complete the question. Choose from the options provided.

6 'The influence of Florence Nightingale was the main reason for improvements in British hospital care c1800–c1900.' How far do you agree? Explain your answer.

You may use the following in your answer:
* death rates at Scutari
* Pasteur's germ theory
You **must** also use information of your own.

(Total for Question 6 = 16 marks + 4 SPaG marks)

* public health during the Boer War
* death rates at Scutari
* the National Insurance Act
* Pasteur's germ theory
* blood transfusion
* the work of Florey and Chain
* Rose Days

3 Use the stimulus points to complete the statement appropriately.

Suggested answer

6 'Jenner's vaccination against smallpox was a major breakthrough in the prevention of disease in Britain during the period c1700–c1900.' How far do you agree? Explain your answer.

You may use the following in your answer:
* cowpox
* cholera
You **must** also use information of your own.

(Total for Question 6 = 16 marks + 4 SPaG marks)

21

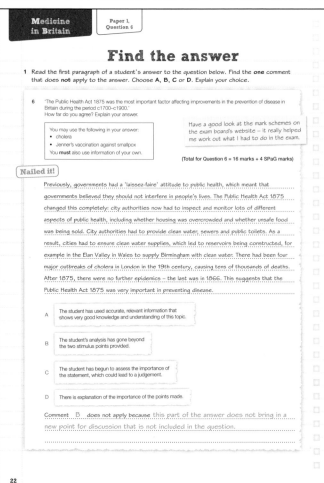

Medicine in Britain — Paper 1, Question 6

Find the answer

1 Read the first paragraph of a student's answer to the question below. Find the **one** comment that does **not** apply to the answer. Choose A, B, C or D. Explain your choice.

6 'The Public Health Act 1875 was the most important factor affecting improvements in the prevention of disease in Britain during the period c1700–c1900.' How far do you agree? Explain your answer.

You may use the following in your answer:
* cholera
* Jenner's vaccination against smallpox
You **must** also use information of your own.

> Have a good look at the mark schemes on the exam board's website – it really helped me work out what I had to do in the exam.

(Total for Question 6 = 16 marks + 4 SPaG marks)

Nailed it!

Previously, governments had a 'laissez-faire' attitude to public health, which meant that governments believed they should not interfere in people's lives. The Public Health Act 1875 changed this completely: city authorities now had to inspect and monitor lots of different aspects of public health, including whether housing was overcrowded and whether unsafe food was being sold. City authorities had to provide clean water, sewers and public toilets. As a result, cities had to ensure clean water supplies, which led to reservoirs being constructed, for example in the Elan Valley in Wales to supply Birmingham with clean water. There had been four major outbreaks of cholera in London in the 19th century, causing tens of thousands of deaths. After 1875, there were no further epidemics – the last was in 1866. This suggests that the Public Health Act 1875 was very important in preventing disease.

A The student has used accurate, relevant information that shows very good knowledge and understanding of this topic.

B The student's analysis has gone beyond the two stimulus points provided.

C The student has begun to assess the importance of the statement, which could lead to a judgement.

D There is explanation of the importance of the points made.

Comment B does not apply because this part of the answer does not bring in a new point for discussion that is not included in the question.

22

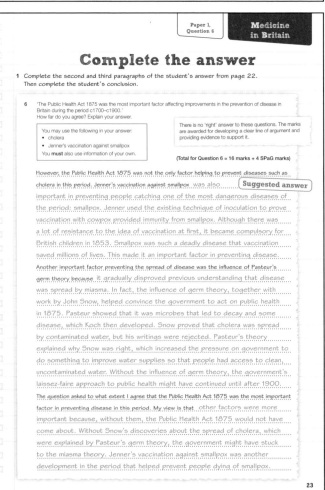

Paper 1, Question 6 — **Medicine in Britain**

Complete the answer

1 Complete the second and third paragraphs of the student's answer from page 22. Then complete the student's conclusion.

6 'The Public Health Act 1875 was the most important factor affecting improvements in the prevention of disease in Britain during the period c1700–c1900.' How far do you agree? Explain your answer.

You may use the following in your answer:
* cholera
* Jenner's vaccination against smallpox
You **must** also use information of your own.

> There is no 'right' answer to these questions. The marks are awarded for developing a clear line of argument and providing evidence to support it.

(Total for Question 6 = 16 marks + 4 SPaG marks)

However, the Public Health Act 1875 was not the only factor helping to prevent diseases such as cholera in this period. Jenner's vaccination against smallpox was also

Suggested answer

important in preventing people catching one of the most dangerous diseases of the period: smallpox. Jenner used the existing technique of inoculation to prove vaccination with cowpox provided immunity from smallpox. Although there was a lot of resistance to the idea of vaccination at first, it became compulsory for British children in 1853. Smallpox was such a deadly disease that vaccination saved millions of lives. This made it an important factor in preventing disease. Another important factor preventing the spread of disease was the influence of Pasteur's germ theory because it gradually disproved previous understanding that disease was spread by miasma. In fact, the influence of germ theory, together with work by John Snow, helped convince the government to act on public health in 1875. Pasteur showed that it was microbes that led to decay and some disease, which Koch then developed. Snow proved that cholera was spread by contaminated water, but his writings were rejected. Pasteur's theory explained why Snow was right, which increased the pressure on government to do something to improve water supplies so that people had access to clean, uncontaminated water. Without the influence of germ theory, the government's laissez-faire approach to public health might have continued until after 1900. The question asked to what extent I agree that the Public Health Act 1875 was the most important factor in preventing disease in this period. My view is that other factors were more important because, without them, the Public Health Act 1875 would not have come about. Without Snow's discoveries about the spread of cholera, which were explained by Pasteur's germ theory, the government might have stuck to the miasma theory. Jenner's vaccination against smallpox was another development in the period that helped prevent people dying of smallpox.

23

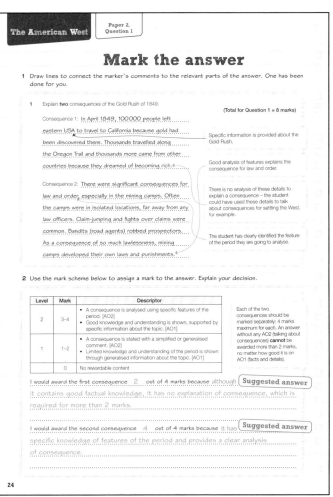

The American West — Paper 2, Question 1

Mark the answer

1 Draw lines to connect the marker's comments to the relevant parts of the answer. One has been done for you.

1 Explain **two** consequences of the Gold Rush of 1849.

(Total for Question 1 = 8 marks)

Consequence 1: In April 1849, 100000 people left eastern USA to travel to California because gold had been discovered there. Thousands travelled along the Oregon Trail and thousands more came from other countries because they dreamed of becoming rich.

→ Specific information is provided about the Gold Rush.

Consequence 2: There were significant consequences for law and order, especially in the mining camps. Often the camps were in isolated locations, far away from any law officers. Claim-jumping and fights over claims were common. Bandits (road agents) robbed prospectors. As a consequence of so much lawlessness, mining camps developed their own laws and punishments.

→ Good analysis of features explains the consequence for law and order.

→ There is no analysis of these details to explain a consequence – the student could have used these details to talk about consequences for settling the West, for example.

→ The student has clearly identified the feature of the period they are going to analyse.

2 Use the mark scheme below to assign a mark to the answer. Explain your decision.

Level	Mark	Descriptor
2	3–4	• A consequence is analysed using specific features of the period. [AO2] • Good knowledge and understanding is shown, supported by specific information about the topic. [AO1]
1	1–2	• A consequence is stated with a simplified or generalised comment. [AO2] • Limited knowledge and understanding of the period is shown through generalised information about the topic. [AO1]
	0	No rewardable content

Each of the two consequences should be marked separately: 4 marks maximum for each. An answer without any AO2 (talking about consequences) **cannot** be awarded more than 2 marks, no matter how good it is on AO1 (facts and details).

I would award the first consequence __2__ out of 4 marks because although **[Suggested answer]** it contains good factual knowledge, it has no explanation of consequence, which is required for more than 2 marks.

I would award the second consequence __4__ out of 4 marks because it has **[Suggested answer]** specific knowledge of features of the period and provides a clear analysis of consequence.

24

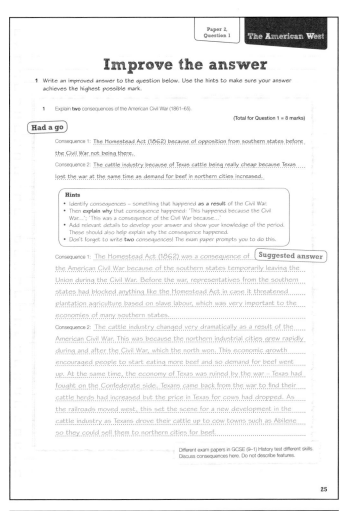

Paper 2, Question 1 — **The American West**

Improve the answer

1 Write an improved answer to the question below. Use the hints to make sure your answer achieves the highest possible mark.

1 Explain **two** consequences of the American Civil War (1861–65).

(Total for Question 1 = 8 marks)

Had a go

Consequence 1: The Homestead Act (1862) because of opposition from southern states before the Civil War not being there.

Consequence 2: The cattle industry because of Texas cattle being really cheap because Texas lost the war at the same time as demand for beef in northern cities increased.

Hints
• Identify consequences – something that happened **as a result** of the Civil War.
• Then **explain why** that consequence happened: 'This happened because the Civil War...'; 'This was a consequence of the Civil War because...'
• Add relevant details to develop your answer and show your knowledge of the period. These should also help explain why the consequence happened.
• Don't forget to write **two** consequences! The exam paper prompts you to do this.

Consequence 1: The Homestead Act (1862) was a consequence of **[Suggested answer]** the American Civil War because of the southern states temporarily leaving the Union during the Civil War. Before the war, representatives from the southern states had blocked anything like the Homestead Act in case it threatened plantation agriculture based on slave labour, which was very important to the economies of many southern states.

Consequence 2: The cattle industry changed very dramatically as a result of the American Civil War. This was because the northern industrial cities grew rapidly during and after the Civil War, which the north won. This economic growth encouraged people to start eating more beef and so demand for beef went up. At the same time, the economy of Texas was ruined by the war – Texas had fought on the Confederate side. Texans came back from the war to find their cattle herds had increased but the price in Texas for cows had dropped. As the railroads moved west, this set the scene for a new development in the cattle industry as Texans drove their cattle up to cow towns such as Abilene so they could sell them to northern cities for beef.

Different exam papers in GCSE (9–1) History test different skills. Discuss consequences here. Do not describe features.

25

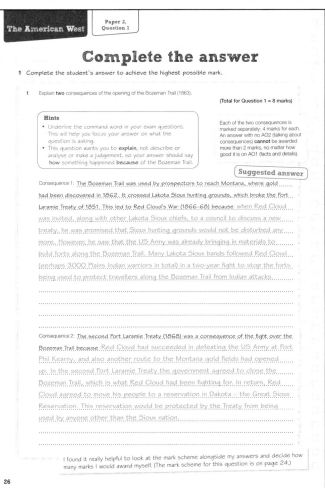

The American West — Paper 2, Question 1

Complete the answer

1 Complete the student's answer to achieve the highest possible mark.

1 Explain **two** consequences of the opening of the Bozeman Trail (1863).

(Total for Question 1 = 8 marks)

Hints
• Underline the command word in your exam questions. This will help you focus your answer on what the question is asking.
• This question wants you to **explain**, not describe or analyse or make a judgement, so your answer should say how something happened **because** of the Bozeman Trail.

Each of the two consequences is marked separately: 4 marks for each. An answer with no AO2 (talking about consequences) **cannot** be awarded more than 2 marks, no matter how good it is on AO1 (facts and details).

[Suggested answer]

Consequence 1: The Bozeman Trail was used by prospectors to reach Montana, where gold had been discovered in 1862. It crossed Lakota Sioux hunting grounds, which broke the Fort Laramie Treaty of 1851. This led to Red Cloud's War (1866–68) because when Red Cloud was invited, along with other Lakota Sioux chiefs, to a council to discuss a new treaty, he was promised that Sioux hunting grounds would not be disturbed any more. However, he saw that the US Army was already bringing in materials to build forts along the Bozeman Trail. Many Lakota Sioux bands followed Red Cloud (perhaps 3000 Plains Indian warriors in total) in a two-year fight to stop the forts being used to protect travellers along the Bozeman Trail from Indian attacks.

Consequence 2: The second Fort Laramie Treaty (1868) was a consequence of the fight over the Bozeman Trail because Red Cloud had succeeded in defeating the US Army at Fort Phil Kearny, and also another route to the Montana gold fields had opened up. In the second Fort Laramie Treaty the government agreed to close the Bozeman Trail, which is what Red Cloud had been fighting for. In return, Red Cloud agreed to move his people to a reservation in Dakota – the Great Sioux Reservation. This reservation would be protected by the Treaty from being used by anyone other than the Sioux nation.

I found it really helpful to look at the mark scheme alongside my answers and decide how many marks I would award myself. (The mark scheme for this question is on page 24.)

26

Paper 2, Question 2 — **The American West**

Re-order the answer

1 A student has written a plan to answer the question below. Number each part (from 1 to 8) to create the best sequence for a successful answer.

2 Write a narrative account analysing the key stages in the growth of the cattle industry in the years 1861–72.

You may use the following in your answer:
• Joseph McCoy and Abilene
• cattle barons
You **must** also use information of your own.

(Total for Question 2 = 8 marks)

4	Joseph McCoy: stockyards, railroad depot; $5000 on marketing in Texas
6	John Iliff: first ranch on open range, by 1870 a cattle baron
3	1867: railroad reached Abilene
1	End of Civil War (1865): huge demand for beef in eastern industrial cities
8	Rise of cattle barons in 1870s: the 'beef bonanza'. Larger and larger herds on open range
2	Impact of Texas fever: Texans couldn't drive cattle across farmland to Missouri railheads
5	Problems of cow towns: law and order, long drives
7	Free grazing land on open range; boom in demand for beef = major increase in investment into cattle ranching

Making a quick plan is a really good idea before you start writing your answer to Question 2 on Paper 2.

Students may choose whether or not to use the prompts suggested in the question. However, students will only be able to access the top-level marks if they include some information of their own.

27

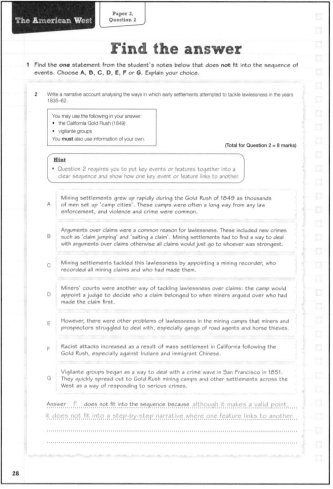

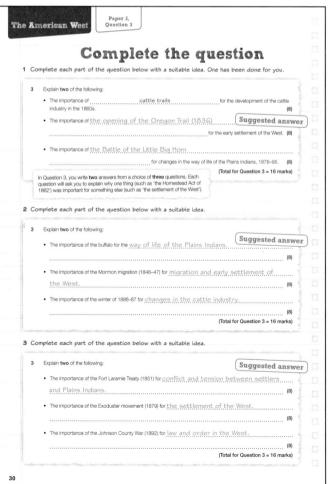

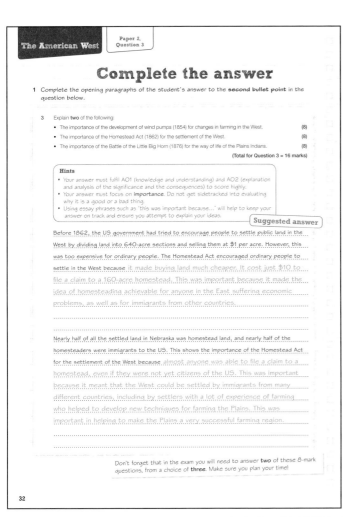

The American West — Paper 2, Question 3

Complete the answer

1 Complete the opening paragraphs of the student's answer to the **second bullet point** in the question below.

3 Explain **two** of the following:
- The importance of the development of wind pumps (1854) for changes in farming in the West. (8)
- The importance of the Homestead Act (1862) for the settlement of the West. (8)
- The importance of the Battle of the Little Big Horn (1876) for the way of life of the Plains Indians. (8)

(Total for Question 3 = 16 marks)

Hints
- Your answer must fulfil AO1 (knowledge and understanding) and AO2 (explanation and analysis of the significance and the consequences) to score highly.
- Your answer must focus on **importance**. Do not get sidetracked into evaluating why it is a good or a bad thing.
- Using essay phrases such as 'this was important because...' will help to keep your answer on track and ensure you attempt to explain your ideas.

Suggested answer

Before 1862, the US government had tried to encourage people to settle public land in the West by dividing land into 640-acre sections and selling them at $1 per acre. However, this was too expensive for ordinary people. The Homestead Act encouraged ordinary people to settle in the West because it made buying land much cheaper. It cost just $10 to file a claim to a 160-acre homestead. This was important because it made the idea of homesteading achievable for anyone in the East suffering economic problems, as well as for immigrants from other countries.

Nearly half of all the settled land in Nebraska was homestead land, and nearly half of the homesteaders were immigrants to the US. This shows the importance of the Homestead Act for the settlement of the West because almost anyone was able to file a claim to a homestead, even if they were not yet citizens of the US. This was important because it meant that the West could be settled by immigrants from many different countries, including by settlers with a lot of experience of farming who helped to develop new techniques for farming the Plains. This was important in helping to make the Plains a very successful farming region.

Don't forget that in the exam you will need to answer **two** of these 8-mark questions, from a choice of **three**. Make sure you plan your time!

32

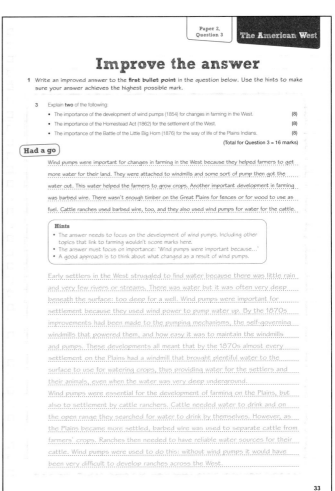

Paper 2, Question 3 — The American West

Improve the answer

1 Write an improved answer to the **first bullet point** in the question below. Use the hints to make sure your answer achieves the highest possible mark.

3 Explain **two** of the following:
- The importance of the development of wind pumps (1854) for changes in farming in the West. (8)
- The importance of the Homestead Act (1862) for the settlement of the West. (8)
- The importance of the Battle of the Little Big Horn (1876) for the way of life of the Plains Indians. (8)

(Total for Question 3 = 16 marks)

Had a go

Wind pumps were important for changes in farming in the West because they helped farmers to get more water for their land. They were attached to windmills and some sort of pump then got the water out. This water helped the farmers to grow crops. Another important development in farming was barbed wire. There wasn't enough timber on the Great Plains for fences or for wood to use as fuel. Cattle ranches used barbed wire, too, and they also used wind pumps for water for the cattle.

Hints
- The answer needs to focus on the development of wind pumps. Including other topics that link to farming wouldn't score marks here.
- The answer must focus on importance: 'Wind pumps were important because...'
- A good approach is to think about what changed as a result of wind pumps.

Early settlers in the West struggled to find water because there was little rain and very few rivers or streams. There was water but it was often very deep beneath the surface: too deep for a well. Wind pumps were important for settlement because they used wind power to pump water up. By the 1870s improvements had been made to the pumping mechanisms, the self-governing windmills that powered them, and how easy it was to maintain the windmills and pumps. These developments all meant that by the 1870s almost every settlement on the Plains had a windmill that brought plentiful water to the surface to use for watering crops, thus providing water for the settlers and their animals, even when the water was very deep underground.

Wind pumps were essential for the development of farming on the Plains, but also to settlement by cattle ranchers. Cattle needed water to drink and on the open range they searched for water to drink by themselves. However, as the Plains became more settled, barbed wire was used to separate cattle from farmers' crops. Ranches then needed to have reliable water sources for their cattle. Wind pumps were used to do this: without wind pumps it would have been very difficult to develop ranches across the West.

33

Superpower relations and the Cold War — Paper 2, Question 1

Mark the answer

1 Draw lines to connect the marker's comments to the relevant parts of the answer. One has been done for you.

1 Explain **two** consequences of the Soviet invasion of Hungary (1956).

(Total for Question 1 = 8 marks)

Consequence 1: In November 1956, Soviet troops invaded Hungary to crush Hungarian opposition to Soviet control, which had followed from reforms introduced by Imre Nagy. Nagy's reforms included free elections that would threaten the control of the Communist Party in Hungary and a plan for Hungary to leave the Warsaw Pact.

Consequence 2: Over 5000 Hungarians died resisting the Soviet invasion, which led to the United Nations condemning Soviet actions. However, the international response was not very strong. A few countries boycotted the 1956 Olympics because the USSR was taking part, but although the US accepted 80000 Hungarian refugees it would not send troops to help Hungarians resist the invasion because of the risk of this turning into nuclear war with the USSR.

Marker's comments:
- Specific information is provided about the Soviet invasion of Hungary.
- One consequence is clearly identified.
- The student has given specific information that explains the consequence.
- The student has explained why there was an invasion rather than explaining what happened **as a result** of the invasion.

2 Use the mark scheme below to assign a mark to the student's answer. Explain your decision.

Level	Mark	Descriptor
2	3–4	• A consequence is analysed using specific features of the period. [AO2] • Good knowledge and understanding is shown, supported by specific information about the topic. [AO1]
1	1–2	• A consequence is stated with a simplified or generalised comment. [AO2] • Limited knowledge and understanding of the period is shown through generalised information about the topic. [AO1]
	0	No rewardable content

Each of the two consequences should be marked separately: 4 marks maximum for each. An answer without any AO2 (talking about consequences) **cannot** be awarded more than 2 marks, no matter how good it is on AO1 (facts and details).

I would award the first consequence 2 out of 4 marks because it contains good factual knowledge but has no focus on consequences.

Suggested answer

I would award the second consequence 4 out of 4 marks because it clearly identifies a consequence and adds specific information to back up the explanation of the consequence.

34

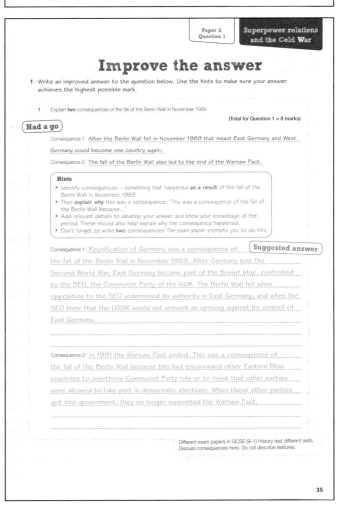

Paper 2, Question 1 — Superpower relations and the Cold War

Improve the answer

1 Write an improved answer to the question below. Use the hints to make sure your answer achieves the highest possible mark.

1 Explain **two** consequences of the fall of the Berlin Wall in November 1989.

(Total for Question 1 = 8 marks)

Had a go

Consequence 1: After the Berlin Wall fell in November 1989 that meant East Germany and West Germany could become one country again.

Consequence 2: The fall of the Berlin Wall also led to the end of the Warsaw Pact.

Hints
- Identify consequences – something that happened **as a result** of the fall of the Berlin Wall in November 1989.
- Then **explain why** this was a consequence: 'This was a consequence of the fall of the Berlin Wall because...'
- Add relevant details to develop your answer and show your knowledge of the period. These should also help explain why the consequence happened.
- Don't forget to write **two** consequences! The exam paper prompts you to do this.

Consequence 1: Reunification of Germany was a consequence of the fall of the Berlin Wall in November 1989. After Germany lost the Second World War, East Germany became part of the Soviet bloc, controlled by the SED, the Communist Party of the GDR. The Berlin Wall fell when opposition to the SED undermined its authority in East Germany, and when the SED knew that the USSR would not prevent an uprising against its control of East Germany.

Suggested answer

Consequence 2: In 1991 the Warsaw Pact ended. This was a consequence of the fall of the Berlin Wall because this had encouraged other Eastern Bloc countries to overthrow Communist Party rule or to insist that other parties were allowed to take part in democratic elections. When these other parties got into government, they no longer supported the Warsaw Pact.

Different exam papers in GCSE (9–1) History test different skills. Discuss consequences here. Do not describe features.

35

Answers

Re-order the answer

1 A student has written a plan to answer the question below. Number each part (from 1 to 7) to create the best sequence for a successful answer. Then add in the correct dates in the spaces provided.

2 Write a narrative account analysing the key events of the Cuban Missile Crisis (1962).

> You may use the following in your answer:
> • Cuban revolution
> • DEFCON 3 (22 October 1962)
> You **must** also use information of your own.

> It's a really good idea to review your plan and order your points before you start writing your answer to Question 2.

(Total for Question 2 = 8 marks)

5 Khrushchev sent a secret message to Kennedy on ___26th October___ 1962. Khrushchev said he was willing to end the crisis. The next day, JFK sent a response agreeing that the US would not invade Cuba if the missiles were removed.

2 The Cuban Missile Crisis began when Soviet nuclear missiles were brought to Cuba in secret. On ___14th October___ 1962, a US U2 spy plane took photographs of missile sites being constructed in Cuba.

4 Khrushchev reacted to Kennedy's decision by describing the US 'blockade' as an act of aggression. He said that Soviet ships would continue to come to Cuba. On ___22nd October___ 1962, DEFCON 3 was declared. This meant that the US thought war was about to start.

7 On ___28th October___ 1962, Khrushchev announced the removal of missiles from Cuba.

1 Cuba had been closely linked to the US. However, the socialist revolution in Cuba in 1959 made the US an enemy of Cuba. In 1961, the US government backed a failed attempt to overthrow Cuba's socialist government by force.

6 To end the crisis, the USSR demanded that the US remove its Jupiter missiles from Turkey. On ___27th October___ 1962, President Kennedy's brother Robert met the Soviet ambassador to the US to agree that this would happen, but that it would not be made public.

3 President Kennedy was advised by his military chiefs to order an air strike on the missile sites, to prevent the threat of an attack on the US, followed by an invasion of Cuba. However, on ___22nd October___, JFK decided on a quarantine to stop any Soviet ships reaching Cuba.

Find the answer

1 Find the **one** statement from the student's notes below that does **not** fit into the sequence of events. Choose A, B, C, D, E, F, G or H. Explain your choice.

2 Write a narrative account analysing the key events of the Soviet response to the Prague Spring (1968).

> You may use the following in your answer:
> • 'socialism with a human face'
> • the Brezhnev Doctrine
> You **must** also use information of your own.

(Total for Question 2 = 8 marks)

A   In January 1968, Alexander Dubcek became leader in Czechoslovakia. He was a friend of Brezhnev and a committed communist.

B   Although Dubcek was a communist, Soviet economic and political methods were very unpopular in Czechoslovakia. Dubcek launched reforms.

C   In the 1980s, Gorbachev's 'new thinking' reforms had similar aims to Dubcek's reforms.

D   Dubcek's reforms aimed for 'socialism with a human face' and relaxed political and economic control. This led to the Prague Spring: more freedom of speech resulted in growing criticism of Soviet control and Soviet communism.

E   Brezhnev was alarmed by the Prague Spring. Other communist leaders in Eastern Europe worried that criticism would spread to their countries and would lead to communist parties losing power there.

F   Brezhnev tried but failed to get Dubcek to bring the reforms under control. In August 1968, the USSR ordered troops into Czechoslovakia. Dubcek was arrested.

G   Czechoslovakia had a new leader: Husak. 'Normalisation' introduced strict Soviet control.

H   The Brezhnev Doctrine: the USSR declared the right to invade any Eastern bloc country that threatened the security of the bloc as a whole.

Answer _C_ does not fit into the sequence because _although it makes a valid point, it does not fit into a step-by-step narrative where one feature links to another._

> Question 2 requires you to put key events or features together into a clear sequence and show how one key event or feature links to another.

Improve the answer

1 Write an improved answer to the question below. Use the hints to make sure your answer achieves the highest possible mark.

2 Write a narrative account analysing key events in the creation of Soviet satellite states in Eastern Europe from 1945 to 1949.

> You may use the following in your answer:
> • the Yalta Conference (1945)
> • 'salami tactics'
> You **must** also use information of your own.

> A narrative account is like a story: it needs a beginning, a middle and an end.

(Total for Question 2 = 8 marks)

Had a go

The USSR thought that Eastern Europe should be in its sphere of influence so Western powers should not have a say in what happened in countries there. In 1946, Churchill made a speech referring to an 'iron curtain' across Europe and warning that the USSR wanted to expand its 'sphere of influence' across Europe. This was important in the development of the Cold War because it added to the US's determination to stop the USSR from taking control, even though in the Yalta conference (1945) the US had agreed to Germany being divided into zones of occupation.

Hints
• The answer so far is not organised into a sequence. Although key events are referred to, they are not all relevant or accurate, and the student has not made links between them.
• Make sure your answer reads as a step-by-step account that leads to an outcome (a result at the end of the process, for example that by 1950 the USSR controlled a bloc of Eastern European countries).

Suggested answer

The Yalta Conference in February 1945 took place during the Second World War, but at a time when the USSR was making rapid progress in the east. The 'Big Three' agreed that after the war there would be free elections in all the countries of Europe that had been under Nazi control. The USSR was confident that people in Eastern Europe would elect Communist Party governments because they had been liberated from the Nazis by the Red Army. However national politicians who had resisted Nazi occupation were very popular and the USSR had to fix elections so that the Communist Party won. It made sure that governments were led by men who would obey Soviet orders. In some cases, such as Hungary, the Communist Party lost the election but then seized power anyway, executing and imprisoning opponents. 'Salami tactics' were used to get rid of opponents to Communist Party control. For example, once Rakosi was in power in Hungary, he set up a secret police force and used it to arrest one group after another, slicing off possible opponents like slicing a salami. The outcome was Soviet satellite states controlled by communist parties that were, in turn, following the orders of the USSR.

Complete the question

1 Complete each part of the question below with a suitable idea. One has been done for you.

3 Explain **two** of the following:

• The importance of US possession of ___the atom bomb___ for relations between the US and the USSR. **(8)**

• The importance of ___the refugee problem___ in Berlin (1958–61) for increasing tensions between East and West. **(8)**

• The importance of ___the Brezhnev Doctrine___ (1968) for Soviet control of Eastern Europe. **(8)**

(Total for Question 3 = 16 marks)

| the Brezhnev Doctrine | ~~the atom bomb~~ | nuclear non-proliferation |
| Tehran Conference | the refugee problem | the formation of NATO |

> In Question 3, you write two answers from a choice of three options. The options will each ask you to explain the importance of **an event/person/development** for a situation or an **unfolding development**.

2 Fill in the missing situation or unfolding development to complete the question. Choose from the options provided.

3 Explain **two** of the following:

• The importance of Cominform (1947) for ___increasing Soviet influence in Eastern Europe.___ **(8)**

• The importance of the launch of Sputnik (1957) for ___the development of the arms race between the US and the USSR.___ **(8)**

• The importance of the 'Velvet Revolution' (1989) for ___the collapse of Soviet control of Eastern Europe.___ **(8)**

(Total for Question 3 = 16 marks)

the collapse of Soviet control of Eastern Europe	increasing Soviet influence in Eastern Europe
increasing de-Stalinisation in Eastern Europe	the US policy of brinkmanship
Soviet relations with Cuba	the development of the arms race between the US and the USSR

> Our teacher gave us a copy of the specification for GCSE (9–1) History at the start of year 10. It was useful to see what we needed to know about different topics.

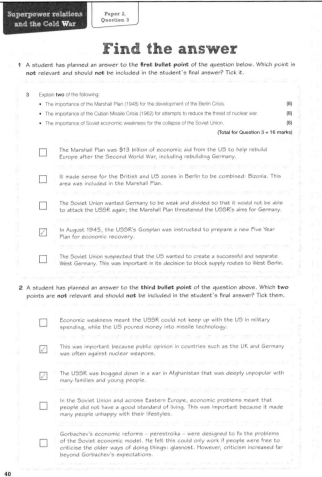

Find the answer

1 A student has planned an answer to the **first bullet point** of the question below. Which point is **not** relevant and should **not** be included in the student's final answer? Tick it.

3 Explain **two** of the following:
- The importance of the Marshall Plan (1948) for the development of the Berlin Crisis. (8)
- The importance of the Cuban Missile Crisis (1962) for attempts to reduce the threat of nuclear war. (8)
- The importance of Soviet economic weakness for the collapse of the Soviet Union. (8)

(Total for Question 3 = 16 marks)

- ☐ The Marshall Plan was $13 billion of economic aid from the US to help rebuild Europe after the Second World War, including rebuilding Germany.
- ☐ It made sense for the British and US zones in Berlin to be combined: Bizonia. This area was included in the Marshall Plan.
- ☐ The Soviet Union wanted Germany to be weak and divided so that it would not be able to attack the USSR again; the Marshall Plan threatened the USSR's aims for Germany.
- ☑ In August 1945, the USSR's Gosplan was instructed to prepare a new Five Year Plan for economic recovery.
- ☐ The Soviet Union suspected that the US wanted to create a successful and separate West Germany. This was important in its decision to block supply routes to West Berlin.

2 A student has planned an answer to the **third bullet point** of the question above. Which **two** points are **not** relevant and should **not** be included in the student's final answer? Tick them.

- ☐ Economic weakness meant the USSR could not keep up with the US in military spending, while the US poured money into missile technology.
- ☑ This was important because public opinion in countries such as the UK and Germany was often against nuclear weapons.
- ☑ The USSR was bogged down in a war in Afghanistan that was deeply unpopular with many families and young people.
- ☐ In the Soviet Union and across Eastern Europe, economic problems meant that people did not have a good standard of living. This was important because it made many people unhappy with their lifestyles.
- ☐ Gorbachev's economic reforms – perestroika – were designed to fix the problems of the Soviet economic model. He felt this could only work if people were free to criticise the older ways of doing things: glasnost. However, criticism increased far beyond Gorbachev's expectations.

40

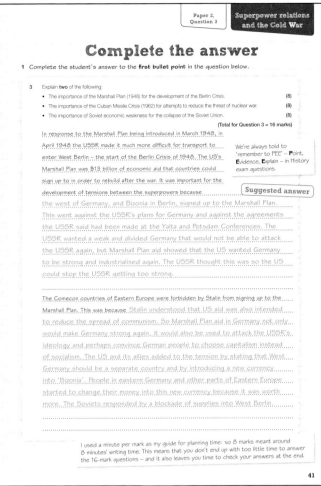

Complete the answer

1 Complete the student's answer to the **first bullet point** in the question below.

3 Explain **two** of the following:
- The importance of the Marshall Plan (1948) for the development of the Berlin Crisis. (8)
- The importance of the Cuban Missile Crisis (1962) for attempts to reduce the threat of nuclear war. (8)
- The importance of Soviet economic weakness for the collapse of the Soviet Union. (8)

(Total for Question 3 = 16 marks)

In response to the Marshall Plan being introduced in March 1948, in April 1948 the USSR made it much more difficult for transport to enter West Berlin – the start of the Berlin Crisis of 1948. The US's Marshall Plan was $13 billion of economic aid that countries could sign up to in order to rebuild after the war. It was important for the development of tensions between the superpowers because

We're always told to 'remember to PEE – Point, Evidence, Explain – in History exam questions.

Suggested answer

the west of Germany, and Bizonia in Berlin, signed up to the Marshall Plan. This went against the USSR's plans for Germany and against the agreements the USSR said had been made at the Yalta and Potsdam Conferences. The USSR wanted a weak and divided Germany that would not be able to attack the USSR again, but Marshall Plan aid showed that the US wanted Germany to be strong and industrialised again. The USSR thought this was so the US could stop the USSR getting too strong.

The Comecon countries of Eastern Europe were forbidden by Stalin from signing up to the Marshall Plan. This was because Stalin understood that US aid was also intended to reduce the spread of communism. So Marshall Plan aid in Germany not only would make Germany strong again, it would also be used to attack the USSR's ideology and perhaps convince German people to choose capitalism instead of socialism. The US and its allies added to the tension by stating that West Germany should be a separate country and by introducing a new currency into 'Bizonia'. People in eastern Germany and other parts of Eastern Europe started to change their money into this new currency because it was worth more. The Soviets responded by a blockade of supplies into West Berlin.

I used a minute per mark as my guide for planning time: so 8 marks meant around 8 minutes' writing time. This means that you don't end up with too little time to answer the 16-mark questions – and it also leaves you time to check your answers at the end.

41

Improve the answer

1 Write an improved answer to the **second bullet point** in the question below. Use the hints to make sure your answer achieves the highest possible mark.

3 Explain **two** of the following:
- The importance of the Marshall Plan (1948) for the development of the Berlin Crisis. (8)
- The importance of the Cuban Missile Crisis (1962) for attempts to reduce the threat of nuclear war. (8)
- The importance of Soviet economic weakness for the collapse of the Soviet Union. (8)

Had a go

(Total for Question 3 = 16 marks)

The Cuban Missile Crisis was about the missiles that the Russians had put on Cuba, very close to the US. When the US found out that the missiles were there, it nearly led to nuclear war. One of the options that President Kennedy had to consider was airstrikes on the missile bases in Cuba. That could have led to a war starting with Russia. So the Cuban Missile Crisis didn't reduce the threat of nuclear war, it increased the threat instead.

Hints
- Answers to these questions have to focus on **importance**: 'the Cuban Missile Crisis was important for attempts to reduce the threat of nuclear war because…'
- This response has not answered the question because the student doesn't include enough knowledge about what happened after the Cuban Missile Crisis.
- Think about what changed as a result of the Cuban Missile Crisis and how this led to the threat of nuclear war being reduced.

Suggested answer

The Cuban Missile Crisis was important for attempts to reduce the threat of nuclear war because both Kennedy and Khrushchev were deeply concerned about how the Cuban Missile Crisis had nearly caused a nuclear war. The Cuban Missile Crisis had ended when Khrushchev announced that the missiles would be removed from Cuba, but the US also agreed in secret to remove nuclear missiles from bases in Turkey, which had threatened the USSR. Both leaders agreed that they needed to be able to communicate directly, because misunderstandings and delayed communications in the Cuban Missile Crisis had added significantly to the risk of nuclear war. As a direct result of the Cuban Missile Crisis, the Hotline Agreement created a direct communication link between the US and USSR, which reduced the chance of nuclear war starting 'by mistake'. Another important consequence was the Limited Test Ban Treaty of 1963. Countries with nuclear weapons had been discussing a ban on testing nuclear weapons for nearly ten years without success, but the Cuban Missile Crisis focused everyone to agree on a solution, even if it was limited in various ways. The Cuban Missile Crisis therefore convinced the superpowers to do more to limit the dangers of nuclear war and the dangers of nuclear weapon testing, even if it did not stop them from developing more and more weapons.

42

Mark the answer

1 Use the mark scheme below to assign a mark to the answer. Explain your decision.

5 (a) Describe **two** features of the Babington plot (1586). (4)

Feature 1: One feature was that Mary, Queen of Scots, was executed after the plot was found out. She was executed by being beheaded.

Feature 2: The plot involved an invasion of England by the Duke of Guise. The plan was for the Duke to kill Elizabeth and put Mary, Queen of Scots, on the throne.

Marking instructions
Each valid feature should be awarded 1 mark, up to a maximum of 2 marks. Each feature should be awarded a second mark for supporting information. E.g. • Mary, Queen of Scots, was involved in the plot (1 mark), which was shown by Babington's letters to Mary (1 mark).

I would award the first feature **1** out of 2 marks because **Suggested answer** there's one valid feature but no supporting information.

I would award the second feature **2** out of 2 marks because there's one valid feature and supporting information.

2 Use the mark scheme below to assign a mark to the answer. Explain your decision.

5 (a) Describe **two** features of Elizabethan society. (4)

Feature 1: One important feature was the Privy Council. This was made up of members of the nobility who helped to govern the country and took account of what was happening in parliament.

Feature 2: There were tenant farmers and also merchants – they could be very wealthy.

Marking instructions
Each valid feature should be awarded 1 mark, up to a maximum of 2 marks. Each feature should be awarded a second mark for supporting information. E.g. • People had to show care for those below them (1 mark). Landowners had a duty of care for their tenants if, for example, there was a harvest failure (1 mark).

I would award the first feature **0** out of 2 marks because the feature **Suggested answer** and supporting information are not relevant: they are about Elizabethan government not Elizabethan society.

I would award the second feature **1** out of 2 marks because there's one valid feature but the supporting information is not detailed enough.

43

85

Early Elizabethan England | Paper 2, Question 5(a)

Complete the question

1 Use the student's answer to complete the question. Include dates where possible.

5 (a) Describe **two** features of Elizabeth's religious settlement (1559) (4)

Nailed it!

Feature 1: A new prayer book was introduced in 1559, called the Book of Common Prayer, which had to be followed by all clergy. The wording in the prayer book was made so that Protestants and Catholics could both use it and understand different things.

Feature 2: A second feature was the Act of Supremacy. Elizabeth was named as Governor of the Church of England. Her father, Henry VIII, had named himself Supreme Head of the Church of England. Governor was a title that showed Elizabeth was more tolerant of religious differences in England.

2 Use the student's answer to complete the question. Include dates where possible.

5 (a) Describe **two** features of the Revolt of the Northern Earls (1569–70) (4)

Nailed it!

Feature 1: Two of the main rebels were Thomas Percy, Earl of Northumberland, and Charles Neville, Earl of Westmorland. Both of them were Catholics who owned huge areas of land in the north, but who had lost a lot of their influence at court.

Feature 2: A second feature was that many northern landowners did not join the revolt, mainly because they had gained a lot of wealth from Henry VIII's dissolution of the monasteries and did not want to have to give it back if England became Catholic again. Examples were landowners in Lancashire and Cheshire.

3 Use the student's answer to complete the question. Include dates where possible.

5 (a) Describe **two** features of the Vagabonds Act (1572) (4)

Nailed it!

Feature 1: Parliament saw vagrants as a threat to public order and wanted to deter vagrancy. Vagrants were whipped and had a hole put in their ears for a first offence, imprisoned if arrested for vagrancy again and given the death penalty for a third offence.

Feature 2: A second feature was helping the 'impotent poor'. A national poor rate was introduced and local authorities (for example, JPs and parish councils) had to keep a poor register and find work for able-bodied poor people.

44

Paper 2, Question 5(a) | **Early Elizabethan England**

Complete the answer

1 Use the marking instructions below to complete the student's answer so that it would be awarded 4 marks.

5 (a) Describe **two** features of the Puritan challenge in the 1560s. (4)

Feature 1: Puritans wanted a simpler style of worship that purified churches of Catholic 'graven images' such as crucifixes and statues, which might encourage **Suggested answer** people to worship religious idols.

Feature 2: Puritans refused to wear the vestments required by the Royal Injunctions because they were not mentioned in the Bible and Puritans thought that only what was in the Bible should be a part of Church services.

Marking instructions
Each valid feature should be awarded 1 mark, up to a maximum of 2 marks. Each feature should be awarded a second mark for supporting information. E.g. • Puritans wanted to live in a 'more godly' society (1 mark). An example of what would make society more 'godly' was banning 'sinful' activities such as gambling or cock fighting (1 mark).

2 Use the marking instructions below to complete the student's answer so that it would be awarded 4 marks.

5 (a) Describe **two** features of school education during Elizabeth's reign (1558–1603). (4)

Feature 1: Parish schools were for children up to the age of 10 years. They were owned by the Church and were run by clergy, usually for the children of **Suggested answer** local yeoman famers and craftsmen.

Feature 2: Grammar schools were for boys aged 10–14 years. They were not run by the Church and charged fees, although poorer families were sometimes awarded scholarships.

Marking instructions
Each valid feature should be awarded 1 mark, up to a maximum of 2 marks. Each feature should be awarded a second mark for supporting information. E.g. • Very few children in Elizabethan England went to school (1 mark). No one believed there was any point educating anyone but the children of rich people, since it was thought no one else would need it (1 mark).

45

Early Elizabethan England | Paper 2, Question 5(b)

Find the answer

1 A student has planned an answer to the question below. Find the **one** point that is **not** accurate, and the one point that is **not** relevant. Explain your choices.

5 (b) Explain why there was an increase in poverty in Elizabethan England, 1558–88. (12)

You may use the following in your answer:
• rural enclosure
• bad harvests
You **must** also use information of your own.

You should only include information that is **accurate** and **relevant** in your answer.

A Enclosure meant poor people couldn't use common land any more.

B Monasteries had helped poor people in the past, but they had been dissolved by Henry VIII in the 1530s.

C England's population grew from 30 million in 1551 to 42 million in 1601.

D People who refused to pay the poor rates could be put in prison after the 1576 Poor Relief Act.

E There were harvest failures in 1562, 1565, 1573 and 1586, which drove up food prices and meant subsistence farmers couldn't grow enough to live on.

The information that I think is not accurate is point C because the **Suggested answer** figures were actually 3 million in 1551 and 4.2 million in 1601.

The information that I think is not relevant is point D because this question is about causes of the increase in poverty, not about policies to tackle the problems of poverty.

2 Find the **one** point of additional information that would **not** help answer the question above. Tick it.

☑ The growth in the triangular trade, developed by John Hawkins

☐ Increasing demand for land due to population increase

☐ Economic recessions caused by trade embargoes

☐ Sheep farming, because it meant less food was grown

Paper 2, Question 5(b) gives you two stimulus points, but you need to add your own information as well as (or instead of) these two points.

46

Paper 2, Question 5(b) | **Early Elizabethan England**

Improve the answer

1 A student has written the first paragraph of an answer to this question. Use the hints below to improve it.

5 (b) Explain why the Spanish Armada was defeated in 1588. (12)

You may use the following in your answer:
• the Battle of Gravelines (8 August 1588)
• the weather
You **must** also use information of your own.

I wish I'd practised writing exam answers in my revision! I learned loads of facts and dates, but sometimes I just wrote down everything I could remember about a topic rather than using what I knew to actually answer the question.

Had a go

The Armada was defeated for many reasons. One was the Battle of Gravelines. Another was that English ships were better armed and equipped. Another was that bad weather hit the Spanish ships when they were trying to retreat. The English had better tactics, too – they could sail close to the Spanish ships and fire on them, but not get so close that the Spanish soldiers on the ships could get across to the English ships. The Battle of Gravelines had fireships. These were important in winning the battle, which the English did, led by Francis Drake.

Hints
• Focus on **explaining** – the answer so far has too much description. • Make a clear argument. The answer above is not very clear. Draw attention to the points you are making by using one paragraph per point and saying things like 'A second reason was that…' • For each point you make, say why this point helps to explain the defeat of the Armada. • Support your points with detail or examples that show you understand this topic.

One important reason for the defeat of the Spanish Armada **Suggested answer** was the superior tactics of the English. The experienced English sailors could manoeuvre their smaller ships around the Spanish ships, staying far enough away to prevent being boarded by Spanish troops, but coming close enough to fire on the Spanish. This was important because it meant the English caused more damage to the Spanish while avoiding damage themselves. Tactics were very important in the Battle of Gravelines (8 August 1588) when the English used fireships (old ships set alight and sailed into the Armada fleet). Many Spanish captains panicked when they saw the fireships coming towards them. To get away as fast as possible they cut their anchors and drifted away. This was important for the defeat because it meant the Spanish Armada lost its organisation and this made it much harder for the Spanish captains to communicate an effective plan of attack (or retreat).

47

Early Elizabethan England — Paper 2, Question 5(b)

Mark the answer

1 Draw lines to connect the marker's comments to the relevant parts of the answer. One has been done for you.

5 (b) Explain why Drake circumnavigated the globe (1577–80). (12)

> You may use the following in your answer:
> • the Battle of San Juan de Ulúa (1568)
> • profits
> You **must** also use information of your own.

The main reason why Francis Drake sailed round the world was not because he was an explorer but because he planned to steal treasure from the Spanish. The Spanish were mining silver and gold in South America (the Spanish Main) and then shipping it back to Spain. Drake intercepted Spanish treasure ships and stole tons of silver and gold – in fact 26 tons of silver and half a ton of gold, as well as jewels and other treasure. However, Drake could not return to England with his treasure, across the Atlantic, because Spanish ships were waiting for him. He went up the west coast of the Americas, tried to find a way back east through the North-West passage but couldn't find it (it was only a myth then), and so was forced to try to sail back west, through Indonesia and round Africa.

This suggests that the most important reason for Drake's voyage was profit. He had an excellent record as a privateer and that meant many rich people were prepared to invest in his voyage, in return for a share of the profits. When Drake finally got back to England in September 1580, Elizabeth's share of the profits was more than enough to pay off England's national debt at the time. It was this enormous profit that made Drake so famous.

Marker's comments:
- Evidence of analytical explanation, as the student is considering which reasons might be more important than others. Let's see if this gets developed later.
- Detailed knowledge shown here; shame the student did not link more closely to the question, e.g. as evidence of profits from the raids for investors.
- Clear focus on the question from the start of the answer. Introduces own knowledge and understanding: potential for Level 4.
- The student is spending far too much time describing what Drake did here: I can't give this any marks because it isn't explaining anything.
- Excellent use of AO1 knowledge to support an AO2 analytical explanation.

48

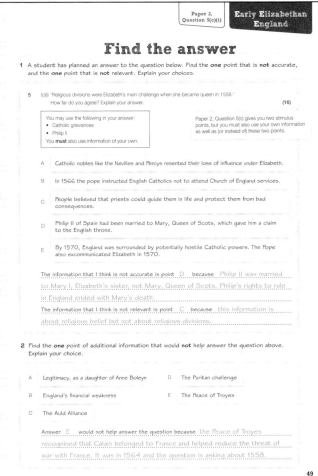

Early Elizabethan England — Paper 2, Question 5(c)(i)

Find the answer

1 A student has planned an answer to the question below. Find the **one** point that is **not** accurate, and the **one** point that is **not** relevant. Explain your choices.

5 (c)(i) 'Religious divisions were Elizabeth's main challenge when she became queen in 1558.' How far do you agree? Explain your answer. (16)

> You may use the following in your answer:
> • Catholic grievances
> • Philip II
> You **must** also use information of your own.

> Paper 2, Question 5(c) gives you two stimulus points, but you must also use your own information as well as (or instead of) these two points.

A Catholic nobles like the Nevilles and Percys resented their loss of influence under Elizabeth.

B In 1566 the pope instructed English Catholics not to attend Church of England services.

C People believed that priests could guide them in life and protect them from bad consequences.

D Philip II of Spain had been married to Mary, Queen of Scots, which gave him a claim to the English throne.

E By 1570, England was surrounded by potentially hostile Catholic powers. The Pope also excommunicated Elizabeth in 1570.

The information that I think is not accurate is point **D** because Philip II was married to Mary I, Elizabeth's sister, not Mary, Queen of Scots. Philip's rights to rule in England ended with Mary's death.

The information that I think is not relevant is point **C** because this information is about religious belief but not about religious divisions.

2 Find the **one** point of additional information that would **not** help answer the question above. Explain your choice.

A Legitimacy, as a daughter of Anne Boleyn
B England's financial weakness
C The Auld Alliance
D The Puritan challenge
E The Peace of Troyes

Answer **E** would not help answer the question because the Peace of Troyes recognised that Calais belonged to France and helped reduce the threat of war with France. It was in 1564 and the question is asking about 1558.

49

Early Elizabethan England — Paper 2, Question 5(c)(i)

Re-order the answer

1 A student has written a plan to answer this 5(c)(i) question. Decide which of their points support the statement below and which counter it. Mark each with an S (support) or a C (counter). One has been done for you.

5 (c)(i) 'Religious divisions were Elizabeth's main challenge when she became queen in 1558.' How far do you agree? Explain your answer. (16)

> You may use the following in your answer:
> • Catholic grievances
> • Philip II
> You **must** also use information of your own.

> **Hint**
> • In deciding 'How far do you agree?' for question 5(c)(i) and (ii), you should consider points that support the statement and points that do not support, or counter, the statement. You then use this evidence to reach your overall judgement.

S One of Elizabeth's first acts as queen was the religious settlement of 1559, which tried to establish a form of religion that would be acceptable to both Protestants and Catholics. This shows how important it was to her to deal with religious differences.

C There were very significant financial problems in 1558: the Crown was £300,000 in debt and debasing the value of England's coinage had resulted in inflation.

C When Anne Boleyn was executed in 1536, Henry VIII had excluded Elizabeth from the succession. Although he reversed this decision before his death, many people continued to doubt Elizabeth's legitimacy.

S As well as Catholic grievances, Elizabeth also faced a Puritan challenge to her religious settlement.

S In 1566, the Pope instructed English Catholics that they were not to attend Church of England services.

S Mary, Queen of Scots, was a focus for Catholic plots against Elizabeth because she was a Catholic with a legitimate claim to the throne.

> These questions are worth 16 marks, so I tried to leave plenty of time to tackle them properly.

50

Early Elizabethan England — Paper 2, Question 5(c)(i)

Complete the answer

1 Use the prompts below to complete the first two paragraphs of the student's answer.

5 (c)(i) 'Religious divisions were Elizabeth's main challenge when she became queen in 1558.' How far do you agree? Explain your answer. (16)

> You may use the following in your answer:
> • Catholic grievances
> • Philip II
> You **must** also use information of your own.

> For questions like this, you don't just have to write about the issue in the question. It's asking you if religious divisions were **most** important, so you need to discuss the other challenges Elizabeth faced as well and then explain which was most significant.

Catholic challenges to her rule were major problems for Elizabeth, both from Catholics in England and from European Catholic nations such as France and Spain. Catholics in England refused to acknowledge Elizabeth's right to rule England because *[Suggested answer]* Elizabeth's mother, Anne Boleyn, was Henry VIII's wife after Henry had divorced Catherine of Aragon. Religious divisions between Catholics, Protestants and Puritans made England a difficult country to rule. One of Elizabeth's first acts as queen was the religious settlement of 1559, which tried to establish a form of religion that would be acceptable to both Protestants and Catholics. The fact that Elizabeth acted on religious divisions so soon after becoming queen is a strong argument for it being the main challenge facing her. However, the religious settlement meant that this challenge was quickly dealt with, which could allow other challenges to be viewed as more important.

However, Catholic grievances and Puritan opposition were not the only challenges facing Elizabeth when she became queen. There were very significant financial problems: the Crown was £300,000 in debt and debasing the value of England's coinage had resulted in inflation. The financial position was a challenge for Elizabeth because she needed money to reward her followers. Without money to do this, her hold on the throne would be seriously weakened. She would also struggle to defend England from invasion by European Catholic countries such as Spain without money to pay for ships and soldiers. That made financial problems a very significant issue for Elizabeth to deal with if she wanted to stay queen. However, the easiest way of raising money – increasing taxation – would be very unpopular with English people and could risk a revolt against her rule of the country. Elizabeth took a different route: she cut down on the extravagant spending of the royal household. She also sold Crown lands, raising £120,000. This meant that by the early 1570s, the Crown was out of debt and the challenge from financial issues was significantly reduced.

51

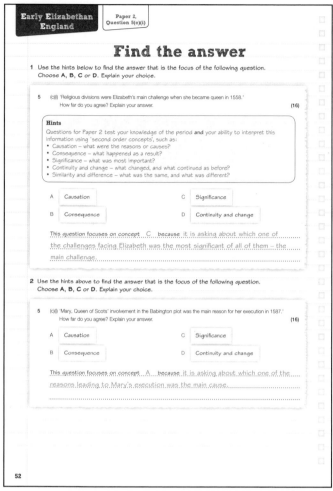

Find the answer

1 Use the hints below to find the answer that is the focus of the following question. Choose A, B, C or D. Explain your choice.

5 (c)(i) 'Religious divisions were Elizabeth's main challenge when she became queen in 1558.'
How far do you agree? Explain your answer. (16)

Hints
Questions for Paper 2 test your knowledge of the period **and** your ability to interpret this information using 'second order concepts', such as:
• Causation – what were the reasons or causes?
• Consequence – what happened as a result?
• Significance – what was most important?
• Continuity and change – what changed, and what continued as before?
• Similarity and difference – what was the same, and what was different?

A Causation   C Significance

B Consequence   D Continuity and change

This question focuses on concept C because it is asking about which one of the challenges facing Elizabeth was the most significant of all of them – the main challenge.

2 Use the hints above to find the answer that is the focus of the following question. Choose A, B, C or D. Explain your choice.

5 (c)(i) 'Mary, Queen of Scots' involvement in the Babington plot was the main reason for her execution in 1587.'
How far do you agree? Explain your answer. (16)

A Causation   C Significance

B Consequence   D Continuity and change

This question focuses on concept A because it is asking about which one of the reasons leading to Mary's execution was the main cause.

52

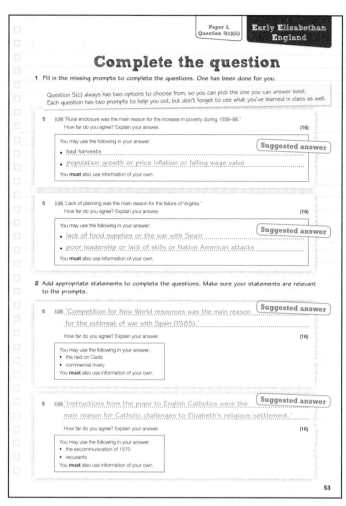

Complete the question

1 Fill in the missing prompts to complete the questions. One has been done for you.

Question 5(c) always has two options to choose from, so you can pick the one you can answer best. Each question has two prompts to help you out, but don't forget to use what you've learned in class as well.

5 (c)(ii) 'Rural enclosure was the main reason for the increase in poverty during 1558–88.'
How far do you agree? Explain your answer. (16)

You may use the following in your answer:
• bad harvests
• population growth or price inflation or falling wage value
You **must** also use information of your own.

Suggested answer

5 (c)(ii) 'Lack of planning was the main reason for the failure of Virginia.'
How far do you agree? Explain your answer. (16)

You may use the following in your answer:
• lack of food supplies or the war with Spain
• poor leadership or lack of skills or Native American attacks
You **must** also use information of your own.

Suggested answer

2 Add appropriate statements to complete the questions. Make sure your statements are relevant to the prompts.

5 (c)(ii) 'Competition for New World resources was the main reason for the outbreak of war with Spain (1585).'

Suggested answer

How far do you agree? Explain your answer. (16)

You may use the following in your answer:
• the raid on Cadiz
• commercial rivalry
You **must** also use information of your own.

5 (c)(ii) 'Instructions from the pope to English Catholics were the main reason for Catholic challenges to Elizabeth's religious settlement.'

Suggested answer

How far do you agree? Explain your answer. (16)

You may use the following in your answer:
• the excommunication of 1570
• recusants
You **must** also use information of your own.

53

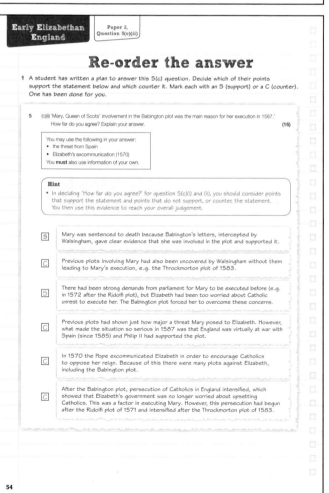

Re-order the answer

1 A student has written a plan to answer this 5(c) question. Decide which of their points support the statement below and which counter it. Mark each with an S (support) or a C (counter). One has been done for you.

5 (c)(ii) 'Mary, Queen of Scots' involvement in the Babington plot was the main reason for her execution in 1587.'
How far do you agree? Explain your answer. (16)

You may use the following in your answer:
• the threat from Spain
• Elizabeth's excommunication (1570)
You **must** also use information of your own.

Hint
• In deciding 'How far do you agree?' for question 5(c)(i) and (ii), you should consider points that support the statement and points that do not support, or counter, the statement. You then use this evidence to reach your overall judgement.

S Mary was sentenced to death because Babington's letters, intercepted by Walsingham, gave clear evidence that she was involved in the plot and supported it.

C Previous plots involving Mary had also been uncovered by Walsingham without them leading to Mary's execution, e.g. the Throckmorton plot of 1583.

S There had been strong demands from parliament for Mary to be executed before (e.g. in 1572 after the Ridolfi plot), but Elizabeth had been too worried about Catholic unrest to execute her. The Babington plot forced her to overcome these concerns.

C Previous plots had shown just how major a threat Mary posed to Elizabeth. However, what made the situation so serious in 1587 was that England was virtually at war with Spain (since 1585) and Philip II had supported the plot.

C In 1570 the Pope excommunicated Elizabeth in order to encourage Catholics to oppose her reign. Because of this there were many plots against Elizabeth, including the Babington plot.

C After the Babington plot, persecution of Catholics in England intensified, which showed that Elizabeth's government was no longer worried about upsetting Catholics. This was a factor in executing Mary. However, this persecution had begun after the Ridolfi plot of 1571 and intensified after the Throckmorton plot of 1583.

54

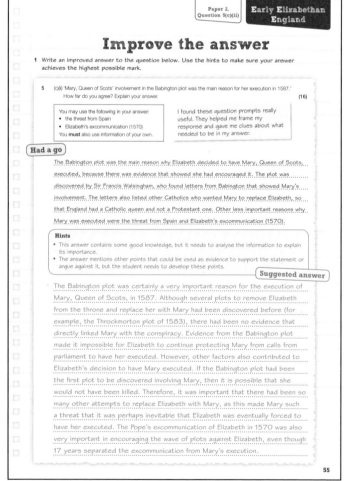

Improve the answer

1 Write an improved answer to the question below. Use the hints to make sure your answer achieves the highest possible mark.

5 (c)(ii) 'Mary, Queen of Scots' involvement in the Babington plot was the main reason for her execution in 1587.'
How far do you agree? Explain your answer. (16)

You may use the following in your answer:
• the threat from Spain
• Elizabeth's excommunication (1570)
You **must** also use information of your own.

I found these question prompts really useful. They helped me frame my response and gave me clues about what needed to be in my answer.

Had a go

The Babington plot was the main reason why Elizabeth decided to have Mary, Queen of Scots, executed, because there was evidence that showed she had encouraged it. The plot was discovered by Sir Francis Walsingham, who found letters from Babington that showed Mary's involvement. The letters also listed other Catholics who wanted Mary to replace Elizabeth, so that England had a Catholic queen and not a Protestant one. Other less important reasons why Mary was executed were the threat from Spain and Elizabeth's excommunication (1570).

Hints
• This answer contains some good knowledge, but it needs to analyse the information to explain its importance.
• The answer mentions other points that could be used as evidence to support the statement or argue against it, but the student needs to develop these points.

Suggested answer

The Babington plot was certainly a very important reason for the execution of Mary, Queen of Scots, in 1587. Although several plots to remove Elizabeth from the throne and replace her with Mary had been discovered before (for example, the Throckmorton plot of 1583), there had been no evidence that directly linked Mary with the conspiracy. Evidence from the Babington plot made it impossible for Elizabeth to continue protecting Mary from calls from parliament to have her executed. However, other factors also contributed to Elizabeth's decision to have Mary executed. If the Babington plot had been the first plot to be discovered involving Mary, then it is possible that she would not have been killed. Therefore, it was important that there had been so many other attempts to replace Elizabeth with Mary, as this made Mary such a threat that it was perhaps inevitable that Elizabeth was eventually forced to have her executed. The Pope's excommunication of Elizabeth in 1570 was also very important in encouraging the wave of plots against Elizabeth, even though 17 years separated the excommunication from Mary's execution.

55

Early Elizabethan England — Paper 2, Question 5(c)(ii)

Mark the answer

1 This simplified mark scheme for Question 5(c) has some information missing. Complete it by putting the information below into the correct gaps. One has been done for you.

Accurate and relevant information is included that shows good understanding of the topic.

There is explanation of why reasons were important, very clear to read and linking to the question all the way through.

There is an overall judgement with some justification, but the justifications aren't always very good.

There is an overall judgement that is fully justified in a convincing way.

There is explanation of why reasons were important, but the explanation doesn't really link to the question.

The answer doesn't make any judgement at all.

Some accurate and relevant information is included.

~~The answer is very simple and not at all developed.~~

> The more you get to know what examiners are looking for, the better your answers will become.

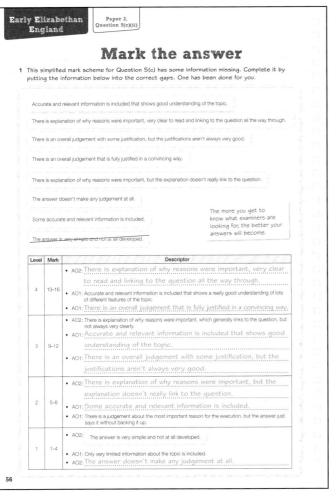

Level	Mark	Descriptor
4	13–16	• AO2: There is explanation of why reasons were important, very clear to read and linking to the question all the way through. • AO1: Accurate and relevant information is included that shows a really good understanding of lots of different features of the topic. • AO1: There is an overall judgement that is fully justified in a convincing way.
3	9–12	• AO2: There is explanation of why reasons were important, which generally links to the question, but not always very clearly. • AO1: Accurate and relevant information is included that shows good understanding of the topic. • AO1: There is an overall judgement with some justification, but the justifications aren't always very good.
2	5–8	• AO2: There is explanation of why reasons were important, but the explanation doesn't really link to the question. • AO1: Some accurate and relevant information is included. • AO1: There is a judgement about the most important reason for the execution, but the answer just says it without backing it up.
1	1–4	• AO2: The answer is very simple and not at all developed. • AO1: Only very limited information about the topic is included. • AO2: The answer doesn't make any judgement at all.

Weimar and Nazi Germany — Paper 3, Question 1

Complete the answer

1 Complete the student's answer so that it would be awarded 4 marks.

Study Source C below and then answer Question 1.

Source C: A picture by Wolfgang Willrich in 1938 showing the ideal Aryan family.

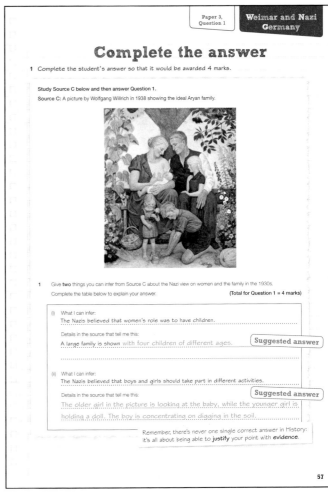

1 Give **two** things you can infer from Source C about the Nazi view on women and the family in the 1930s.
Complete the table below to explain your answer.
(Total for Question 1 = 4 marks)

(i) What I can infer:
The Nazis believed that women's role was to have children.

Details in the source that tell me this:
A large family is shown with four children of different ages. **[Suggested answer]**

(ii) What I can infer:
The Nazis believed that boys and girls should take part in different activities.

Details in the source that tell me this: **[Suggested answer]**
The older girl in the picture is looking at the baby, while the younger girl is holding a doll. The boy is concentrating on digging in the soil.

> Remember, there's never one single correct answer in History: it's all about being able to **justify** your point with **evidence**.

Weimar and Nazi Germany — Paper 3, Question 1

Mark the answer

1 Draw lines to connect the marker's comments to the relevant parts of the answer.

Study Source D below and then answer Question 1.

Source D: From a Ministry of Propaganda order, March 1934

> Attention! On Wednesday 21st March, the Führer is speaking on all German [radio] stations from 11am to 11:50am ... All factory owners, stores, offices, shops, pubs and flats must put up speakers an hour before, so that the whole workforce can hear.

1 Give **two** things you can infer from Source D about how the Nazis used media to influence people's attitudes.
Complete the table below to explain your answer.
(Total for Question 1 = 4 marks)

(i) What I can infer:
Radio was important for Nazi propaganda.

Details in the source that tell me this:
The Nazis used different media for propaganda, including newspapers, plays, art, books and films. Yet radio was the most important, perhaps because lots of people had a radio in their house (this was before TVs) and on the radio people could listen to Hitler actually talking, which was a powerful experience.

This is not a valid inference: the student has identified information provided by the source rather than going beyond what the source says.

This is a valid inference to make for 1 mark.

Unfortunately, the student has not backed up the valid inference with supporting detail selected from the source. Instead, they have used their own knowledge to explain why radio was important. No marks can be awarded for this.

(ii) What I can infer:
There was an important speech by Hitler on 21st March 1934.

Details in the source that tell me this:
It gives the date in the source and also the time so people knew they had to listen.

This is not a convincing supporting statement to back up a point about importance. Selecting relevant quotes from the source would have been a better approach here.

Hints

Examiners are always looking for ways to give you marks if they possibly can, which is why it is better to write something rather than nothing.
- The 4 marks available for Question 1 are split into 2 marks for each inference.
- The first mark is for identifying a valid inference – something that you can correctly infer from the source. This should not be something that is stated directly.
- The second mark is for supporting detail to back up the inference. That detail needs to come from the source.
- A good way to back up an inference is to use a quote from the source.

Weimar and Nazi Germany — Paper 3, Question 2

Find the answer

1 Find the **one** point of additional information that would help answer the question below. Choose **A, B, C** or **D**. Explain your choice.

2 Explain why there was an economic recovery in the Weimar Republic in the period 1924–29.

> You may use the following in your answer:
> • the introduction of the Rentenmark
> • American loans
> You **must** also use information of your own.

(Total for Question 2 = 12 marks)

A   The Treaty of Versailles

B   Labour service

C   Rearmament

D   The Dawes Plan

> Question 2 asks the student to explain why a change happened. The question provides two stimulus points with suggested topics to write about, but in order to get more than 8 marks out of the 12 available, the student must include information of their own.

> I thought the more I wrote, the more marks I'd get but examiners are looking for really specific things – and waffle isn't one of them!

Answer D would be the correct choice because the Treaty of Versailles was earlier (1919) and a cause of economic problems, while labour service and rearmament were Nazi policies of the 1930s.

2 Find the **one** point of additional information that would **not** help answer the question below. Choose **A, B, C** or **D**. Explain your choice.

2 Explain why there were changes in the lives of women in Nazi Germany 1933–39.

> You may use the following in your answer:
> • Nazi organisations for women and girls
> • the introduction of marriage loans
> You **must** also use information of your own.

(Total for Question 2 = 12 marks)

A   The League of German Maidens

B   Nazi ideals on women's clothing, hair and use of make-up

C   Awards for numbers of children

D   Kinder, Küche, Kirche

Answer A would not help answer the question because the League of German Maidens was a Nazi organisation for women and girls and so it is already covered in the first stimulus point; it's not additional information.

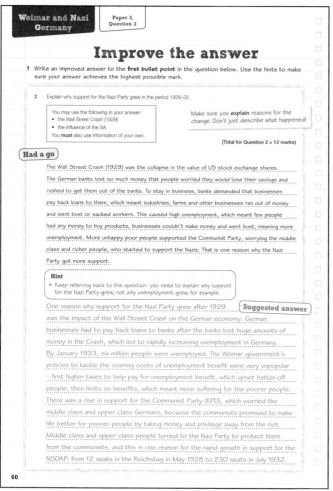

Improve the answer

1 Write an improved answer to the **first bullet point** in the question below. Use the hints to make sure your answer achieves the highest possible mark.

2 Explain why support for the Nazi Party grew in the period 1929–32.

> You may use the following in your answer:
> • the Wall Street Crash (1929)
> • the influence of the SA
> You **must** also use information of your own.

Make sure you **explain** reasons for the change. Don't just describe what happened!

(Total for Question 2 = 12 marks)

Had a go

The Wall Street Crash (1929) was the collapse in the value of US stock exchange shares. The German banks lost so much money that people worried they would lose their savings and rushed to get them out of the banks. To stay in business, banks demanded that businesses pay back loans to them, which meant industries, farms and other businesses ran out of money and went bust or sacked workers. This caused high unemployment, which meant few people had any money to buy products, businesses couldn't make money and went bust, meaning more unemployment. More unhappy poor people supported the Communist Party, worrying the middle class and richer people, who started to support the Nazis. That is one reason why the Nazi Party got more support.

Hint
• Keep referring back to the question: you need to explain why support for the Nazi Party grew, not why unemployment grew, for example.

Suggested answer

One reason why support for the Nazi Party grew after 1929 was the impact of the Wall Street Crash on the German economy. German businesses had to pay back loans to banks after the banks lost huge amounts of money in the Crash, which led to rapidly increasing unemployment in Germany. By January 1933, six million people were unemployed. The Weimar government's policies to tackle the soaring costs of unemployment benefit were very unpopular – first higher taxes to help pay for unemployment benefit, which upset better-off people, then limits on benefits, which meant more suffering for the poorer people. There was a rise in support for the Communist Party (KPD), which worried the middle class and upper class Germans, because the communists promised to make life better for poorer people by taking money and privilege away from the rich. Middle class and upper class people turned to the Nazi Party to protect them from the communists, and this is one reason for the rapid growth in support for the NSDAP: from 12 seats in the Reichstag in May 1928 to 230 seats in July 1932.

60

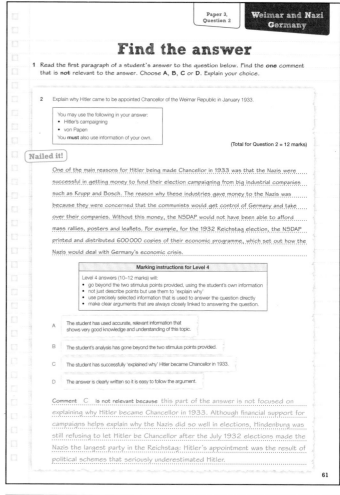

Find the answer

1 Read the first paragraph of a student's answer to the question below. Find the **one** comment that is **not** relevant to the answer. Choose A, B, C or D. Explain your choice.

2 Explain why Hitler came to be appointed Chancellor of the Weimar Republic in January 1933.

> You may use the following in your answer:
> • Hitler's campaigning
> • von Papen
> You **must** also use information of your own.

(Total for Question 2 = 12 marks)

Nailed it!

One of the main reasons for Hitler being made Chancellor in 1933 was that the Nazis were successful in getting money to fund their election campaigning from big industrial companies such as Krupp and Bosch. The reason why these industries gave money to the Nazis was because they were concerned that the communists would get control of Germany and take over their companies. Without this money, the NSDAP would not have been able to afford mass rallies, posters and leaflets. For example, for the 1932 Reichstag election, the NSDAP printed and distributed 600,000 copies of their economic programme, which set out how the Nazis would deal with Germany's economic crisis.

Marking instructions for Level 4
Level 4 answers (10–12 marks) will:
• go beyond the two stimulus points provided, using the student's own information
• not just describe points but use them to 'explain why'
• use precisely selected information that is used to answer the question directly
• make clear arguments that are always closely linked to answering the question.

A   The student has used accurate, relevant information that shows very good knowledge and understanding of this topic.

B   The student's analysis has gone beyond the two stimulus points provided.

C   The student has successfully 'explained why' Hitler became Chancellor in 1933.

D   The answer is clearly written so it is easy to follow the argument.

Comment   C   is not relevant because this part of the answer is not focused on explaining why Hitler became Chancellor in 1933. Although financial support for campaigns helps explain why the Nazis did so well in elections, Hindenburg was still refusing to let Hitler be Chancellor after the July 1932 elections made the Nazis the largest party in the Reichstag; Hitler's appointment was the result of political schemes that seriously underestimated Hitler.

61

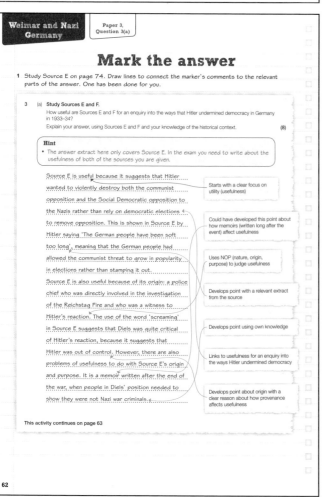

Mark the answer

1 Study Source E on page 74. Draw lines to connect the marker's comments to the relevant parts of the answer. One has been done for you.

3 (a) Study Sources E and F.
How useful are Sources E and F for an enquiry into the ways that Hitler undermined democracy in Germany in 1933–34?
Explain your answer, using Sources E and F and your knowledge of the historical context. (8)

Hint
• The answer extract here only covers Source E. In the exam you need to write about the usefulness of both of the sources you are given.

Source E is useful because it suggests that Hitler wanted to violently destroy both the communist opposition and the Social Democratic opposition to the Nazis rather than rely on democratic elections to remove opposition. This is shown in Source E by Hitler saying 'The German people have been soft too long', meaning that the German people had allowed the communist threat to grow in popularity in elections rather than stamping it out. Source E is also useful because of its origin: a police chief who was directly involved in the investigation of the Reichstag Fire and who was a witness to Hitler's reaction. The use of the word 'screaming' in Source E suggests that Diels was quite critical of Hitler's reaction, because it suggests that Hitler was out of control. However, there are also problems of usefulness to do with Source E's origin and purpose. It is a memoir written after the end of the war, when people in Diels' position needed to show they were not Nazi war criminals.

- Starts with a clear focus on utility (usefulness)
- Could have developed this point about how memoirs (written long after the event) affect usefulness
- Uses NOP (nature, origin, purpose) to judge usefulness
- Develops point with a relevant extract from the source
- Develops point using own knowledge
- Links to usefulness for an enquiry into the ways Hitler undermined democracy
- Develops point about origin with a clear reason about how provenance affects usefulness

This activity continues on page 63

62

Mark the answer

2 Use the mark scheme below to decide at which level the answer on page 62 is working.

Remember, in the exam you should write about both of the sources you are given.

Question	
3(a)	How useful are Sources E and F for an enquiry into the ways that Hitler undermined democracy in Germany in 1933–34? Explain your answer, using Sources E and F and your knowledge of the historical context. **Target:** Analysis and evaluation of source utility. **AO3:** 8 marks.

Level	Descriptor
3	• Judgements about usefulness for the specific enquiry in the question are made, which take account of how provenance* affects the usefulness of the source content. Contextual knowledge is used in interpreting the source and making judgements about usefulness.
2	• Judgements about usefulness for the specific enquiry in the question are made. These judgements are supported by comments that are relevant to the sources. Contextual knowledge is used to support comments on the usefulness of the content of the sources and/or their provenance.
1	• A simple judgement is made about usefulness. Supporting comments about the content of the source or provenance (nature/origin/purpose) are not really developed. The use of contextual knowledge is only limited.
	No rewardable content.

*Provenance = nature, origin, purpose.

I would award the answer a level   3   because, as well as saying how useful Source E is for the specific enquiry (the ways that Hitler undermined democracy in Germany in 1933–34), which takes it to Level 2, it also considers the strengths and weaknesses of provenance (nature, origin and purpose) for the usefulness of this source. It does that by talking about the strengths and weaknesses of memoirs (though this could have been developed further) and by using own knowledge to consider how the problems of being associated with the Nazis could have affected what Diels recorded in this source. That lifts it from Level 2 to Level 3. Contextual knowledge is used but only in a Level 2 way – it is not used to support the interpretation of the source, only to comment on its usefulness.

Suggested answer

63

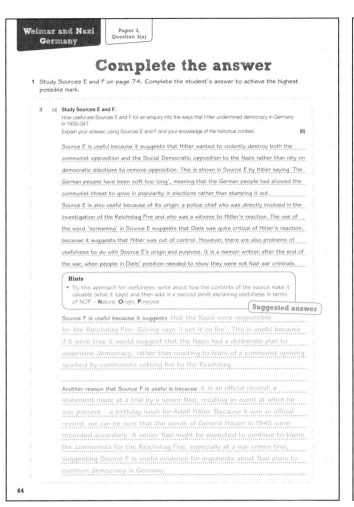

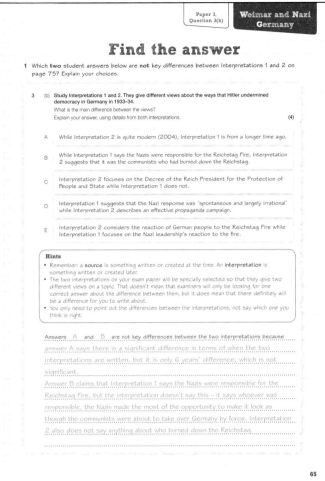

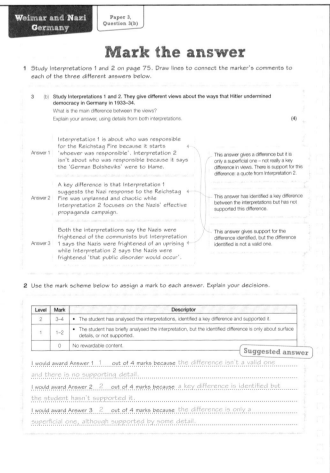

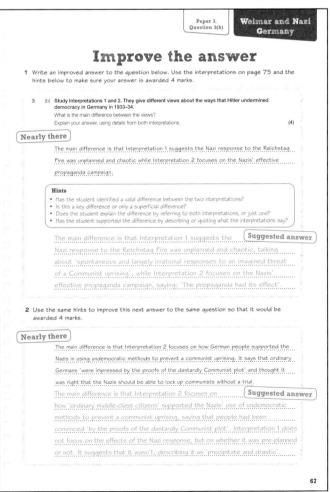

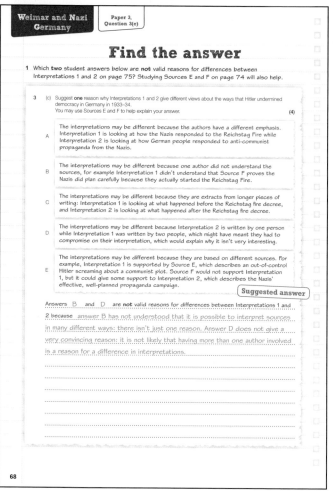

Weimar and Nazi Germany — Paper 3, Question 3(c)

Find the answer

1 Which **two** student answers below are **not** valid reasons for differences between Interpretations 1 and 2 on page 75? Studying Sources E and F on page 74 will also help.

3 (c) Suggest **one** reason why Interpretations 1 and 2 give different views about the ways that Hitler undermined democracy in Germany in 1933–34.
You may use Sources E and F to help explain your answer. (4)

A The interpretations may be different because the authors have a different emphasis. Interpretation 1 is looking at how the Nazis responded to the Reichstag Fire while Interpretation 2 is looking at how German people responded to anti-communist propaganda from the Nazis.

B The interpretations may be different because one author did not understand the sources, for example Interpretation 1 didn't understand that Source F proves the Nazis did plan carefully because they actually started the Reichstag Fire.

C The interpretations may be different because they are extracts from longer pieces of writing: Interpretation 1 is looking at what happened before the Reichstag fire decree, and Interpretation 2 is looking at what happened after the Reichstag fire decree.

D The interpretations may be different because Interpretation 2 is written by one person while Interpretation 1 was written by two people, which might have meant they had to compromise on their interpretation, which would explain why it isn't very interesting.

E The interpretations may be different because they are based on different sources. For example, Interpretation 1 is supported by Source E, which describes an out-of-control Hitler screaming about a communist plot. Source F would not support Interpretation 1, but it could give some support to Interpretation 2, which describes the Nazis' effective, well-planned propaganda campaign.

Suggested answer

Answers B and D are **not** valid reasons for differences between Interpretations 1 and 2 because answer B has not understood that it is possible to interpret sources in many different ways: there isn't just one reason. Answer D does not give a very convincing reason: it is not likely that having more than one author involved is a reason for a difference in interpretations.

68

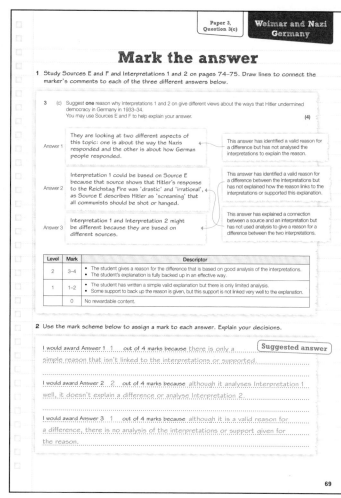

Paper 3, Question 3(c) — **Weimar and Nazi Germany**

Mark the answer

1 Study Sources E and F and Interpretations 1 and 2 on pages 74–75. Draw lines to connect the marker's comments to each of the three different answers below.

3 (c) Suggest **one** reason why Interpretations 1 and 2 on give different views about the ways that Hitler undermined democracy in Germany in 1933–34.
You may use Sources E and F to help explain your answer. (4)

Answer 1: They are looking at two different aspects of this topic: one is about the way the Nazis responded and the other is about how German people responded.
→ This answer has identified a valid reason for a difference but has not analysed the interpretations to explain the reason.

Answer 2: Interpretation 1 could be based on Source E because that source shows that Hitler's response to the Reichstag Fire was 'drastic' and 'irrational', as Source E describes Hitler as 'screaming' that all communists should be shot or hanged.
→ This answer has identified a valid reason for a difference between the interpretations but has not explained how the reason links to the interpretations or supported this explanation.

Answer 3: Interpretation 1 and Interpretation 2 might be different because they are based on different sources.
→ This answer has explained a connection between a source and an interpretation but has not used analysis to give a reason for a difference between the two interpretations.

Level	Mark	Descriptor
2	3–4	• The student gives a reason for the difference that is based on good analysis of the interpretations. • The student's explanation is fully backed up in an effective way.
1	1–2	• The student has written a simple valid explanation but there is only limited analysis. • Some support to back up the reason is given, but this support is not linked very well to the explanation.
	0	No rewardable content.

2 Use the mark scheme below to assign a mark to each answer. Explain your decisions.

Suggested answer

I would award Answer 1 1 out of 4 marks because there is only a simple reason that isn't linked to the interpretations or supported.

I would award Answer 2 2 out of 4 marks because although it analyses Interpretation 1 well, it doesn't explain a difference or analyse Interpretation 2.

I would award Answer 3 1 out of 4 marks because although it is a valid reason for a difference, there is no analysis of the interpretations or support given for the reason.

69

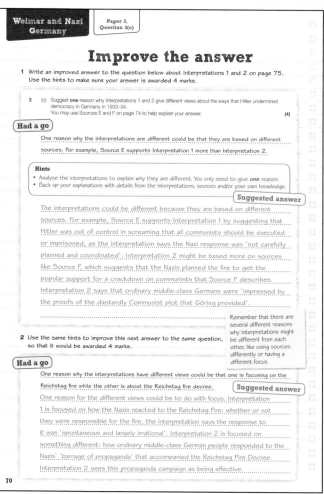

Weimar and Nazi Germany — Paper 3, Question 3(c)

Improve the answer

1 Write an improved answer to the question below about Interpretations 1 and 2 on page 75. Use the hints to make sure your answer is awarded 4 marks.

3 (c) Suggest **one** reason why Interpretations 1 and 2 give different views about the ways that Hitler undermined democracy in Germany in 1933–34.
You may use Sources E and F on page 74 to help explain your answer. (4)

Had a go

One reason why the interpretations are different could be that they are based on different sources. For example, Source E supports Interpretation 1 more than Interpretation 2.

Hints
• Analyse the interpretations to explain why they are different. You only need to give **one** reason.
• Back up your explanations with details from the interpretations, sources and/or your own knowledge.

Suggested answer

The interpretations could be different because they are based on different sources. For example, Source E supports Interpretation 1 by suggesting that Hitler was out of control in screaming that all communists should be executed or imprisoned, as the interpretation says the Nazi response was 'not carefully planned and coordinated'. Interpretation 2 might be based more on sources like Source F, which suggests that the Nazis planned the fire to get the popular support for a crackdown on communists that Source F describes. Interpretation 2 says that ordinary middle-class Germans were 'impressed by the proofs of the dastardly Communist plot that Göring provided'.

Remember that there are several different reasons why interpretations might be different from each other, like using sources differently or having a different focus.

2 Use the same hints to improve this next answer to the same question, so that it would be awarded 4 marks.

Had a go

One reason why the interpretations have different views could be that one is focusing on the Reichstag fire while the other is about the Reichstag fire decree.

Suggested answer

One reason for the different views could be to do with focus. Interpretation 1 is focused on how the Nazis reacted to the Reichstag Fire: whether or not they were responsible for the fire, the interpretation says the response to it was 'spontaneous and largely irrational'. Interpretation 2 is focused on something different: how ordinary middle-class German people responded to the Nazis' 'barrage of propaganda' that accompanied the Reichstag Fire Decree. Interpretation 2 sees this propaganda campaign as being effective.

70

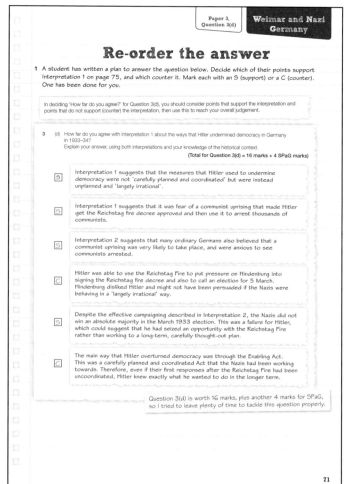

Paper 3, Question 3(d) — **Weimar and Nazi Germany**

Re-order the answer

1 A student has written a plan to answer the question below. Decide which of their points support Interpretation 1 on page 75, and which counter it. Mark each with an S (support) or a C (counter). One has been done for you.

In deciding 'How far do you agree?' for Question 3(d), you should consider points that support the interpretation and points that do not support (counter) the interpretation, then use this to reach your overall judgement.

3 (d) How far do you agree with Interpretation 1 about the ways that Hitler undermined democracy in Germany in 1933–34?
Explain your answer, using both interpretations and your knowledge of the historical context.
(Total for Question 3(d) = 16 marks + 4 SPaG marks)

S — Interpretation 1 suggests that the measures that Hitler used to undermine democracy were not 'carefully planned and coordinated' but were instead unplanned and 'largely irrational'.

S — Interpretation 1 suggests that it was fear of a communist uprising that made Hitler get the Reichstag fire decree approved and then use it to arrest thousands of communists.

S — Interpretation 2 suggests that many ordinary Germans also believed that a communist uprising was very likely to take place, and were anxious to see communists arrested.

C — Hitler was able to use the Reichstag Fire to put pressure on Hindenburg in signing the Reichstag fire decree and also to call an election for 5 March. Hindenburg disliked Hitler and might not have been persuaded if the Nazis were behaving in a 'largely irrational' way.

S — Despite the effective campaigning described in Interpretation 2, the Nazis did not win an absolute majority in the March 1933 election. This was a failure for Hitler, which could suggest that he had seized an opportunity with the Reichstag Fire rather than working to a long-term, carefully thought-out plan.

C — The main way that Hitler overturned democracy was through the Enabling Act. This was a carefully planned and coordinated Act that the Nazis had been working towards. Therefore, even if their first responses after the Reichstag Fire had been uncoordinated, Hitler knew exactly what he wanted to do in the longer term.

Question 3(d) is worth 16 marks, plus another 4 marks for SPaG, so I tried to leave plenty of time to tackle this question properly.

71

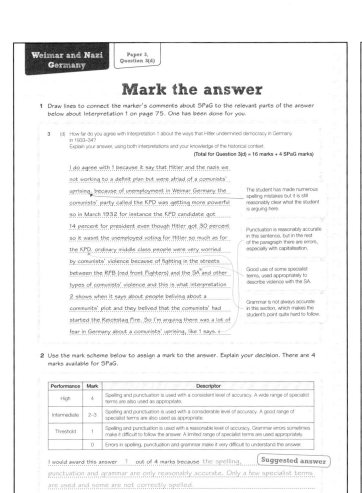

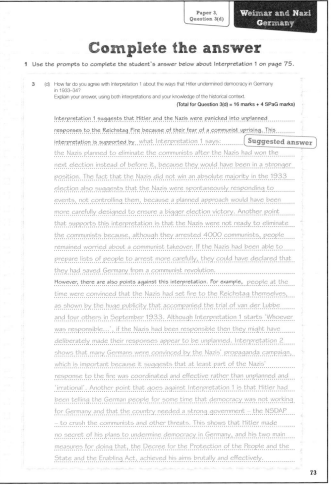

Published by Pearson Education Limited, 80 Strand, London, WC2R 0RL.

www.pearsonschools.co.uk

Text © Pearson Education Limited 2018
Edited, typeset and produced by Elektra Media Ltd
Original illustrations © Pearson Education Limited 2018
Cover illustration by Eoin Coveney

The right of Rob Bircher to be identified as author of this work has been asserted by him in accordance with the Copyright, Designs and Patents Act 1988.

First published 2018

21 20 19 18
10 9 8 7 6 5 4 3 2

British Library Cataloguing in Publication Data
A catalogue record for this book is available from the British Library.

ISBN 978 1 292 23025 2

Printed in Slovakia by Neografia

Acknowledgements
The authors and publisher would like to thank the following individuals and organisations for their kind permission to reproduce copyright material.

Photographs
Alamy Stock Photo: Chronicle 57, 89

All other images © Pearson Education

We would like to thank Joni Sommerville, Theo Mellors, Emily Plenty, John-Paul Duddy, Emily Atkinson, Jess Salmon, Holly Coop, Matthew Foot and David Birch for their invaluable help in providing student tips for the series.

Note from publisher
1. While the publishers have made every attempt to ensure that advice on the qualification and its assessment is accurate, the official specification and associated assessment guidance materials are the only authoritative source of information and should always be referred to for definitive guidance.

Pearson examiners have not contributed to any sections in this resource relevant to examination papers for which they have responsibility.

2. Pearson has robust editorial processes, including answer and fact checks, to ensure the accuracy of the content in this publication, and every effort is made to ensure this publication is free of errors. We are, however, only human, and occasionally errors do occur. Pearson is not liable for any misunderstandings that arise as a result of errors in this publication, but it is our priority to ensure that the content is accurate. If you spot an error, please do contact us at resourcescorrections@pearson.com so we can make sure it is corrected.